Hans-Günter Heumann

Piano Junior

A Creative and Interactive
Piano Course for Children

Performance Book 3

ED 13833

Illustrations by Leopé

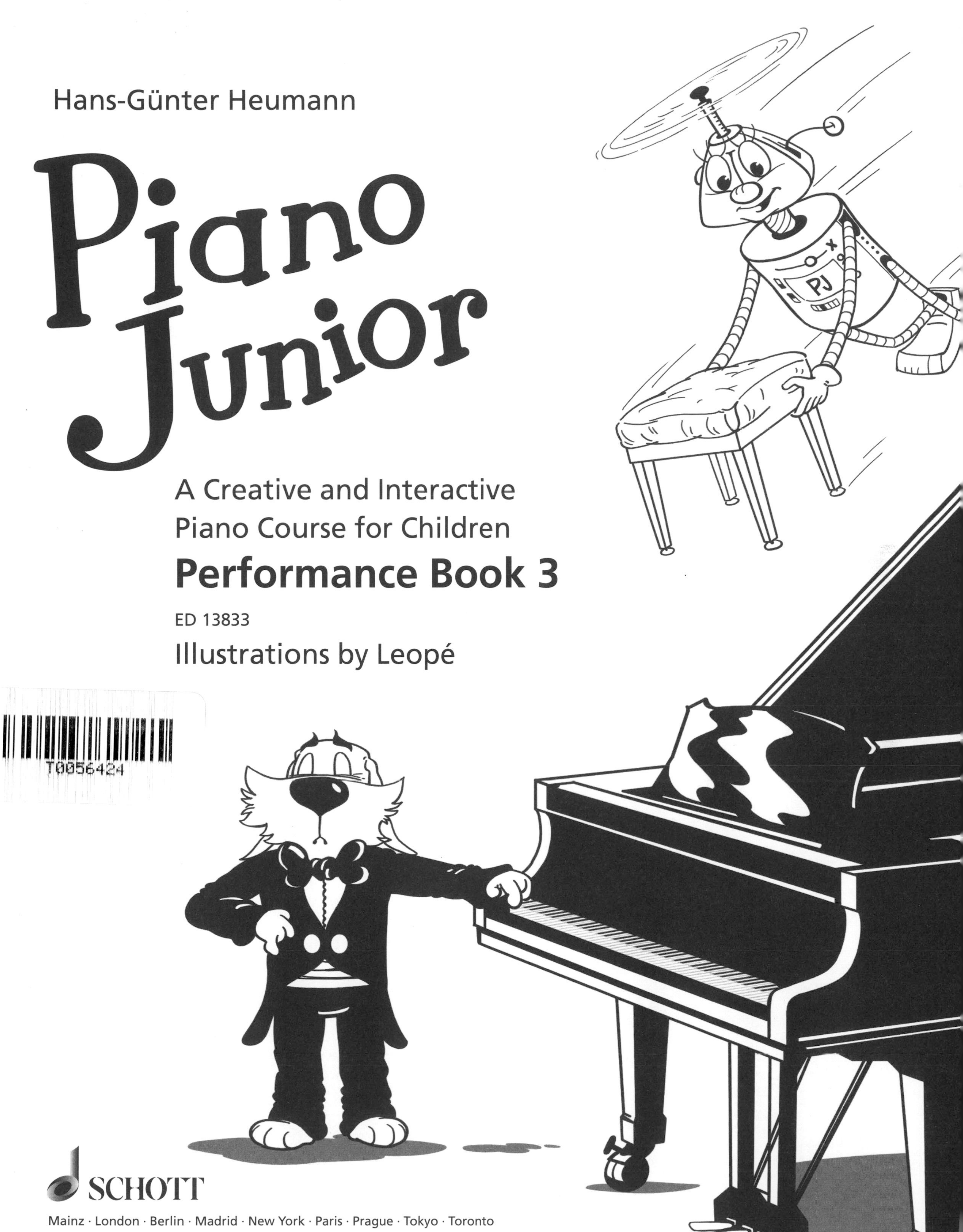

SCHOTT
Mainz · London · Berlin · Madrid · New York · Paris · Prague · Tokyo · Toronto

ED 13833
British Library Cataloguing-in-Publication-Data.
A catalogue record for this book is available from the British Library.
ISMN 979-0-2201-3651-1
ISBN 978-1-84761-436-0

Cover illustration by Leopé (www.leope.com)
Cover photography: iStockphoto
Cover design: www.adamhaystudio.com
Printed in Germany S&Co.9220

Contents

1. Long, Long Ago

Thomas Haynes Bayly (1797–1839)
Arr.: HGH

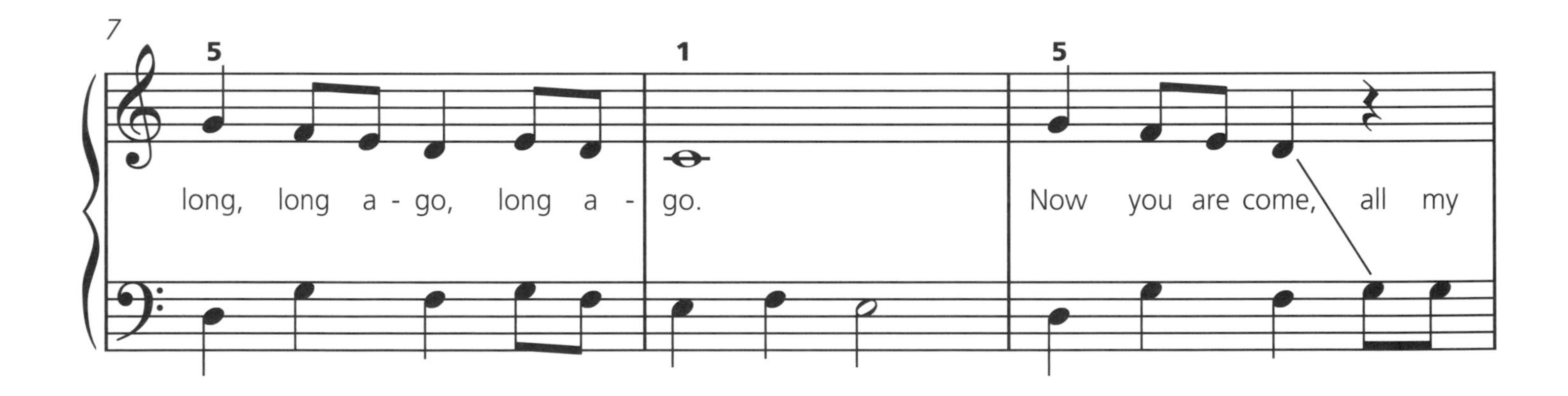

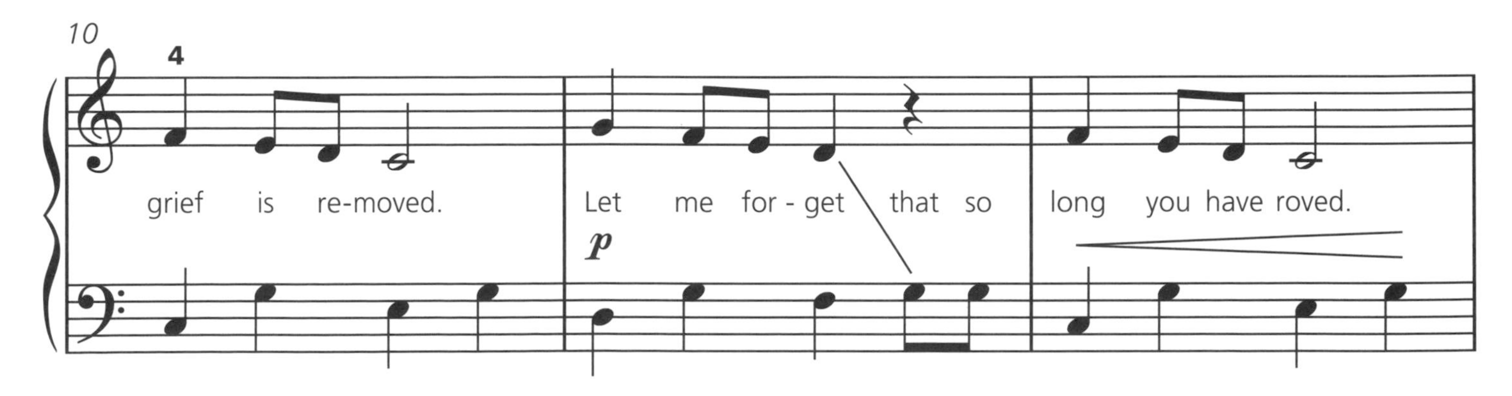

13
rit.
Let me be-lieve that you love as you loved, long, long a - go, long a - go.
mf
PJ
PJ

2. By the Light of the Moon

Au clair de la lune

French Folk Song
Arr.: HGH

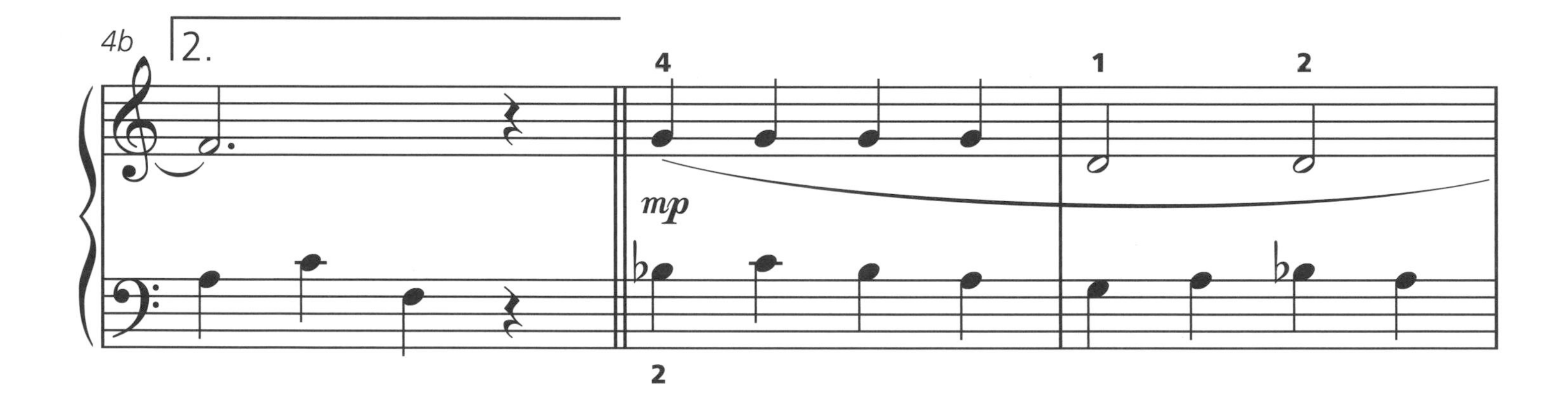

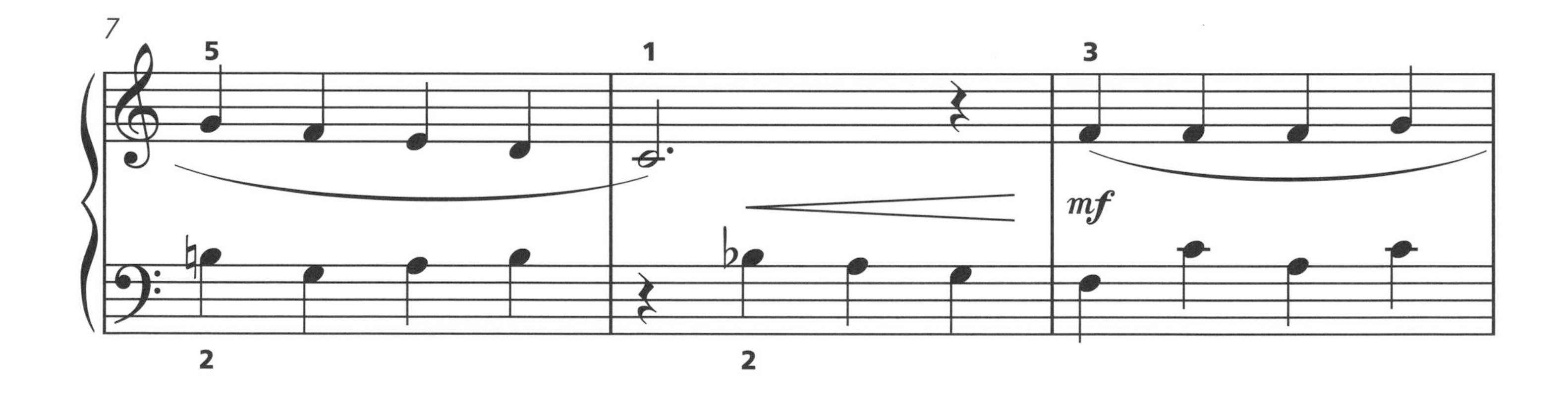

3. Kum Ba Yah*

♩ = 144

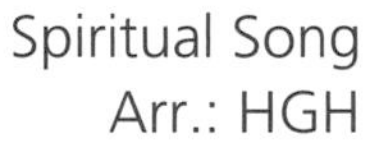

Spiritual Song
Arr.: HGH

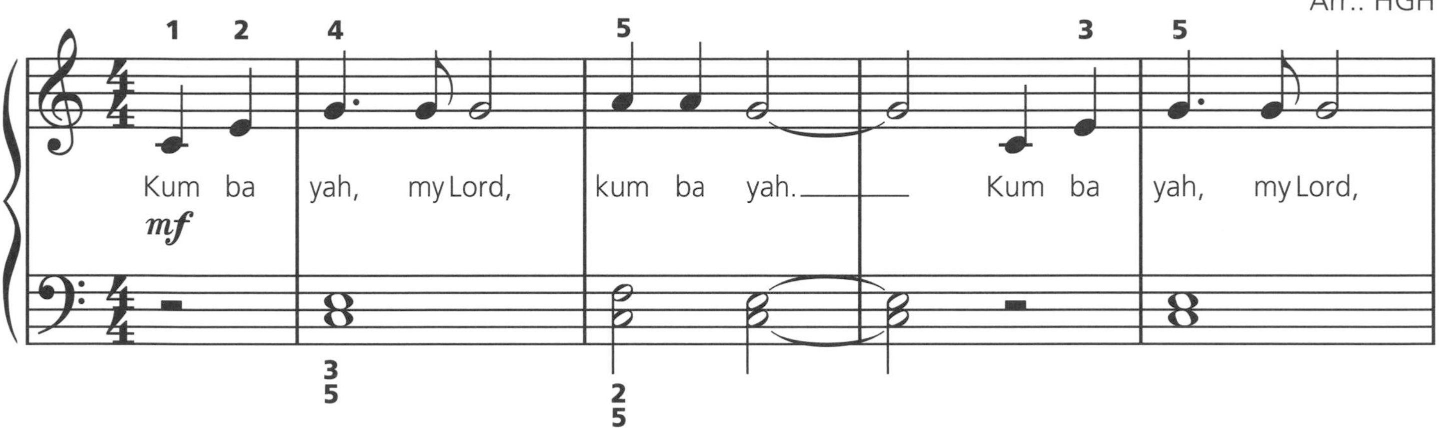

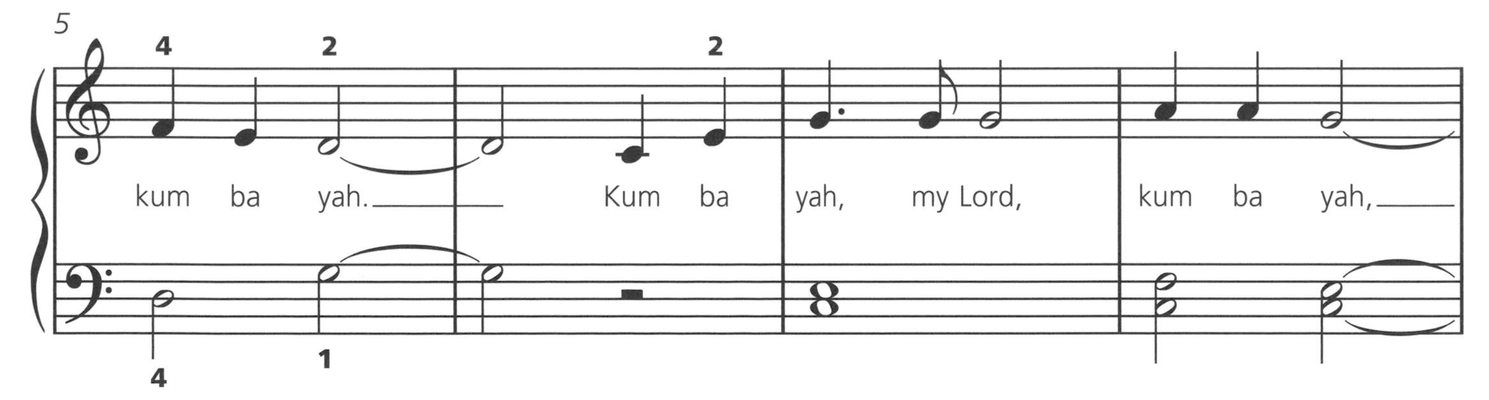

*) **kum ba yah** = Come by here

4. On Top of Old Smoky

Folk Song from the USA
Arr.: HGH

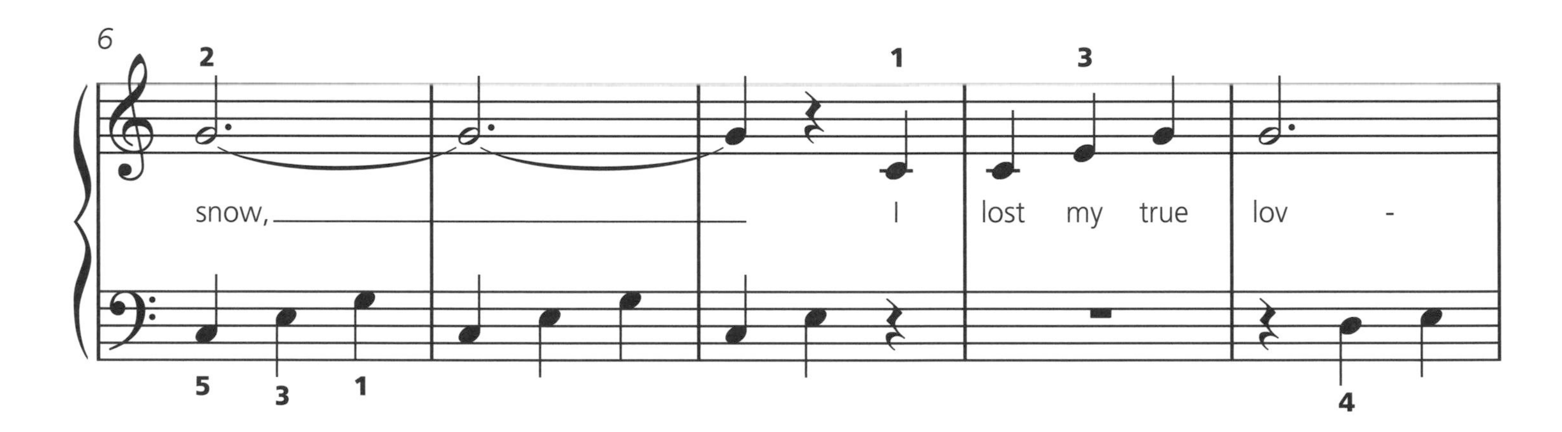

20
and
part - ing
is
grief,

24
a
false - heart - ed
lov - - er
is

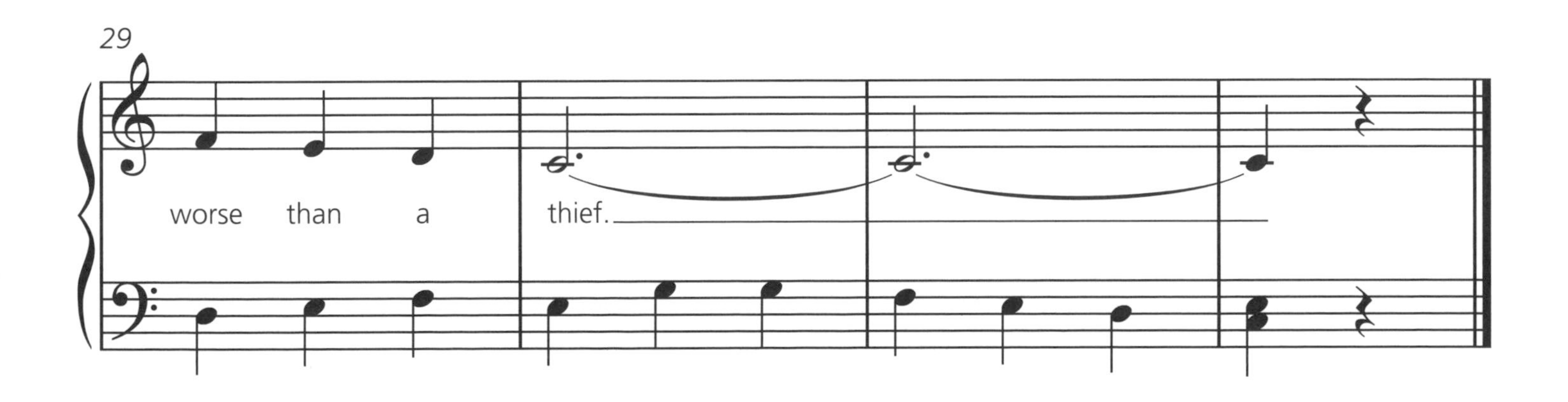
29
worse than a
thief.

5. Lavender's Blue

♩ = 144

Old English Melody, late 17th century
Arr.: HGH

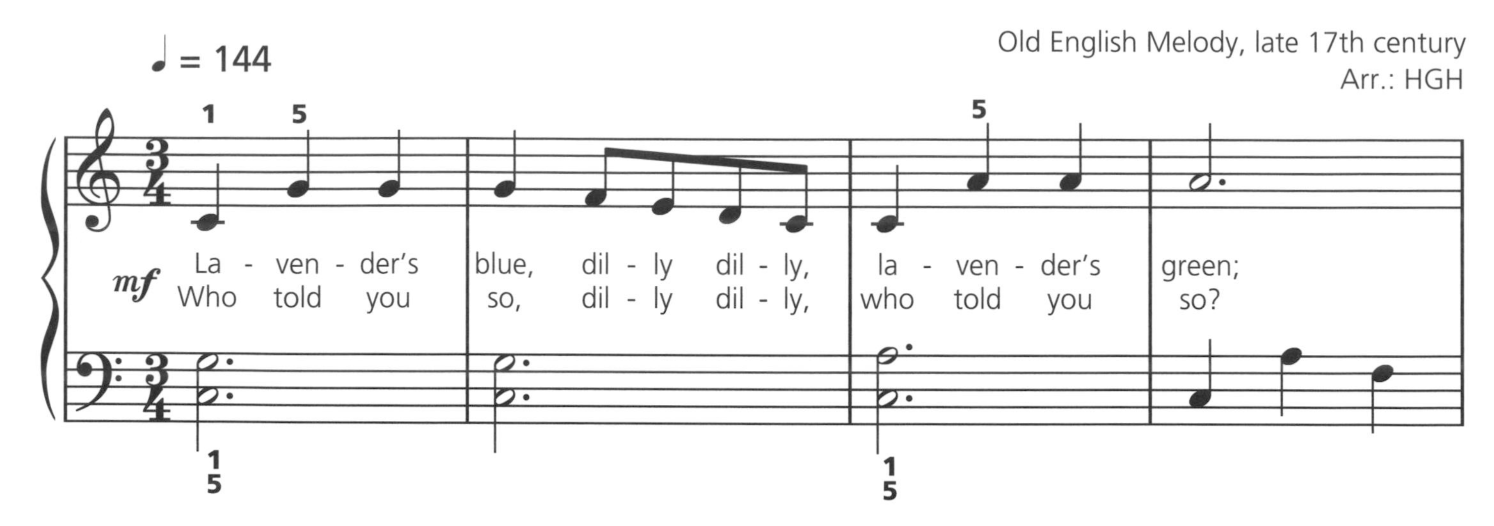

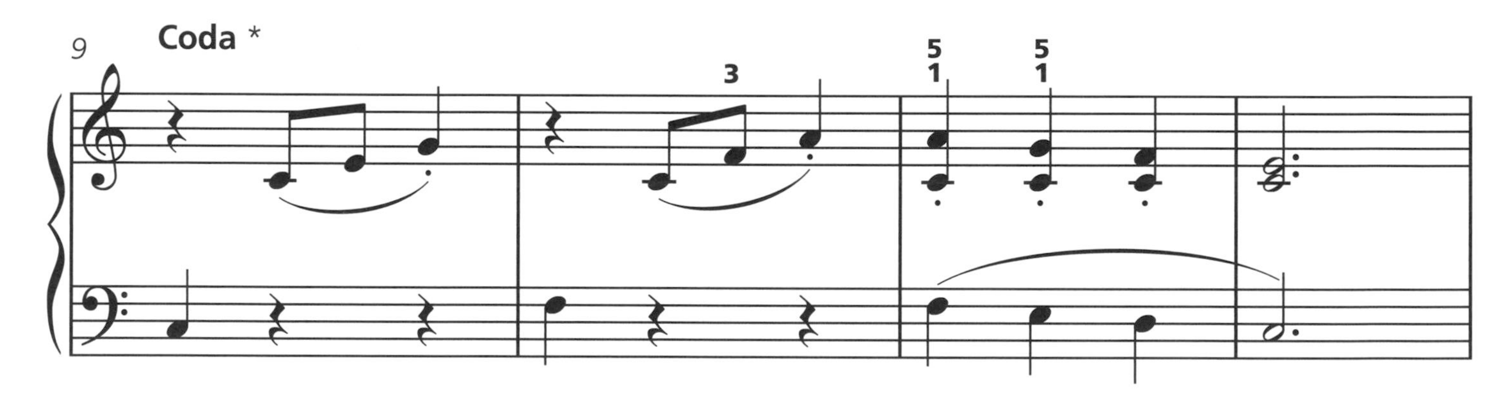

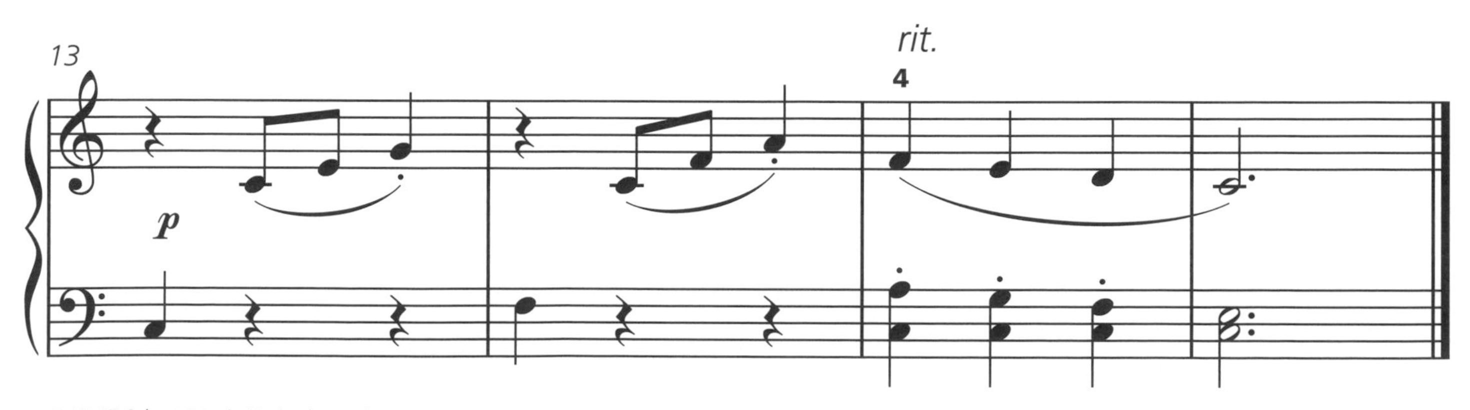

*) **A coda** is a concluding section added at the end of a piece.

6. Allegretto

Op. 139, No. 7

Carl Czerny (1791–1857)

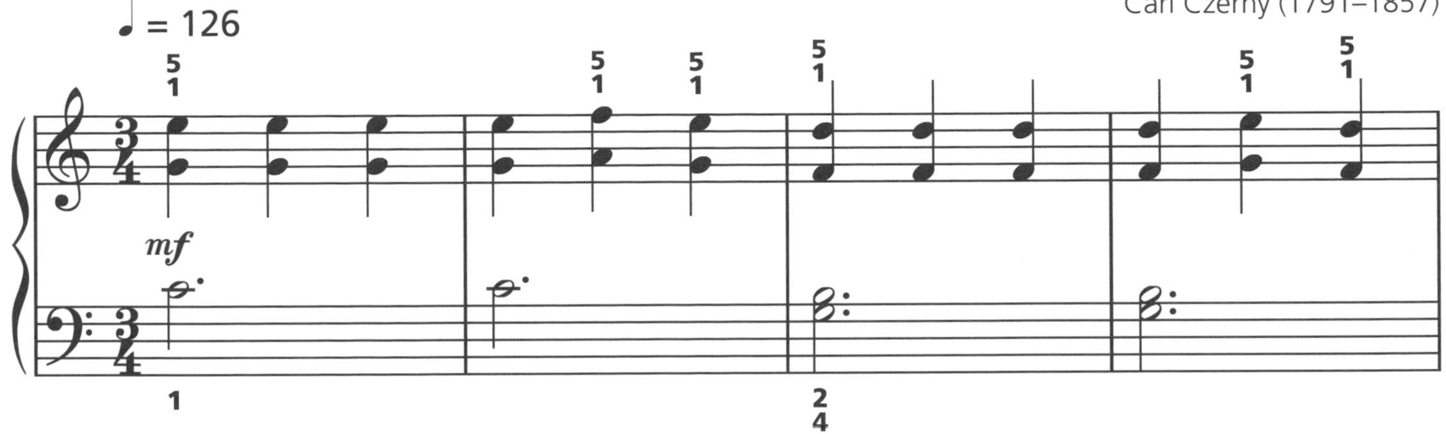

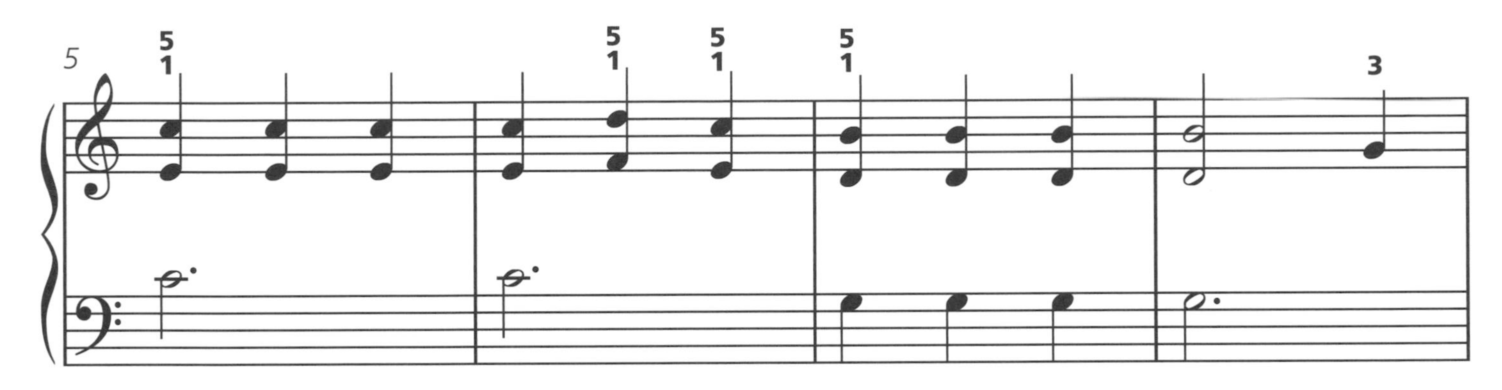

Carl Czerny was an Austrian pianist and piano teacher; he was a pupil of Ludwig van Beethoven and taught Franz Liszt. Czerny wrote a large number of technical exercises and studies for pianists.

7. For He's a Jolly Good Fellow

♩. = 80

Traditional
Arr.: HGH

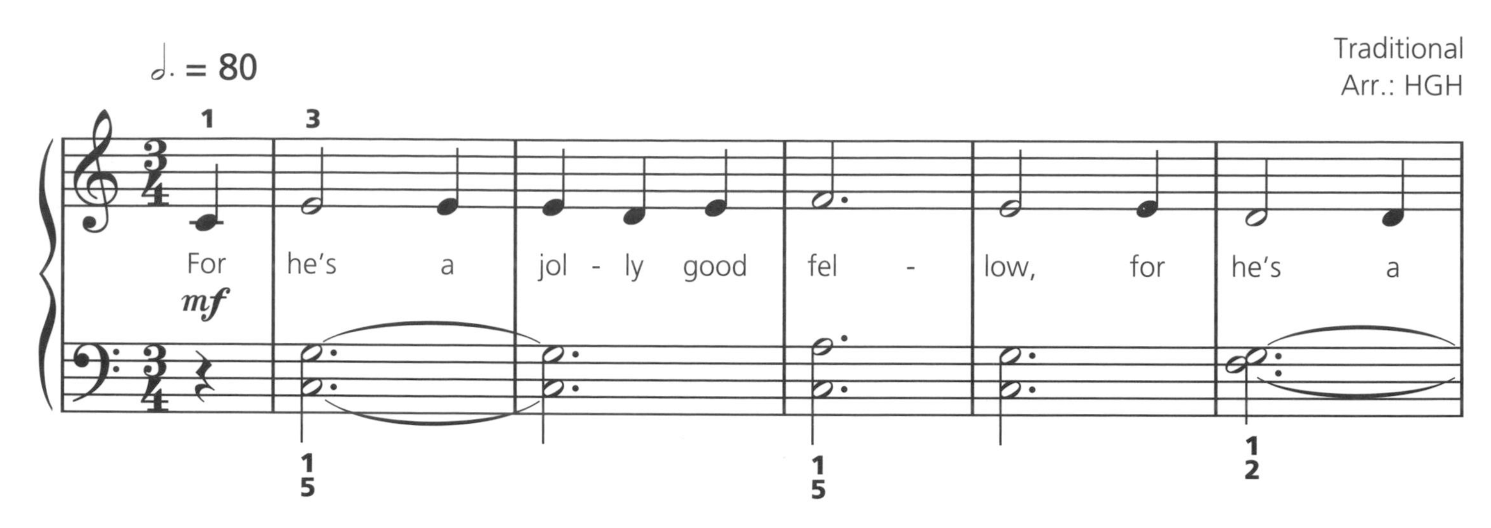

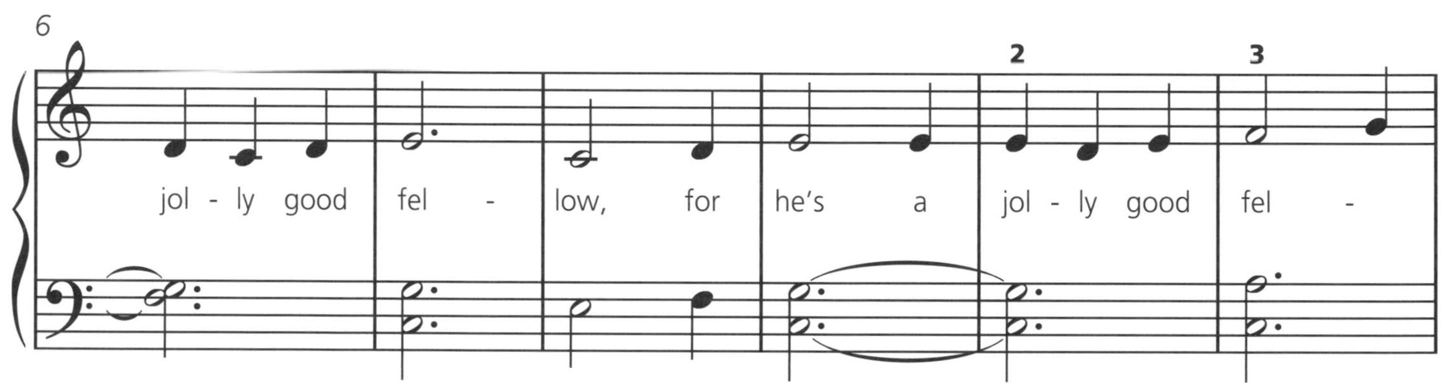

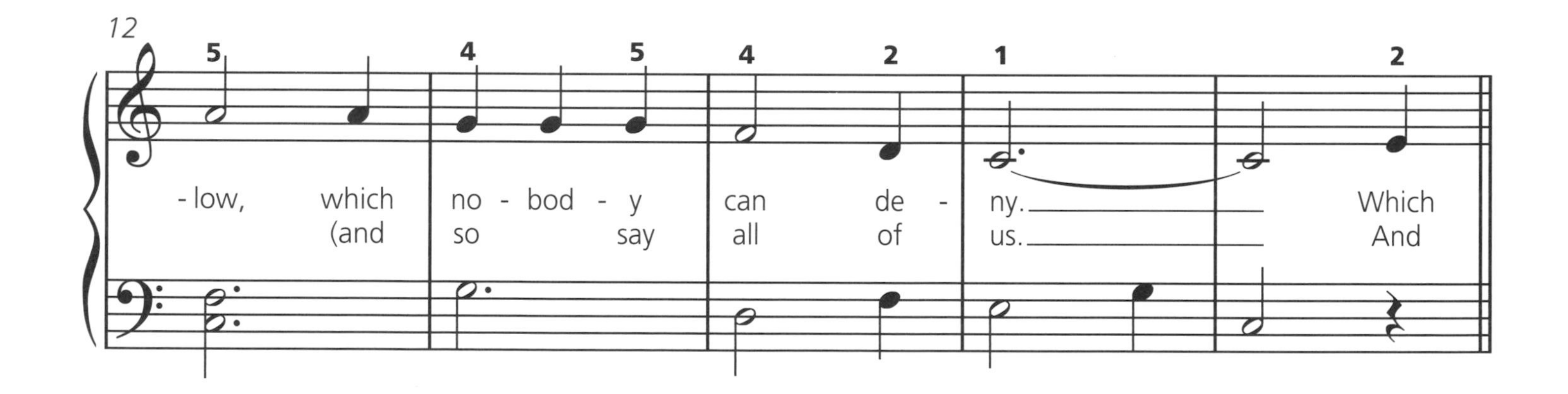

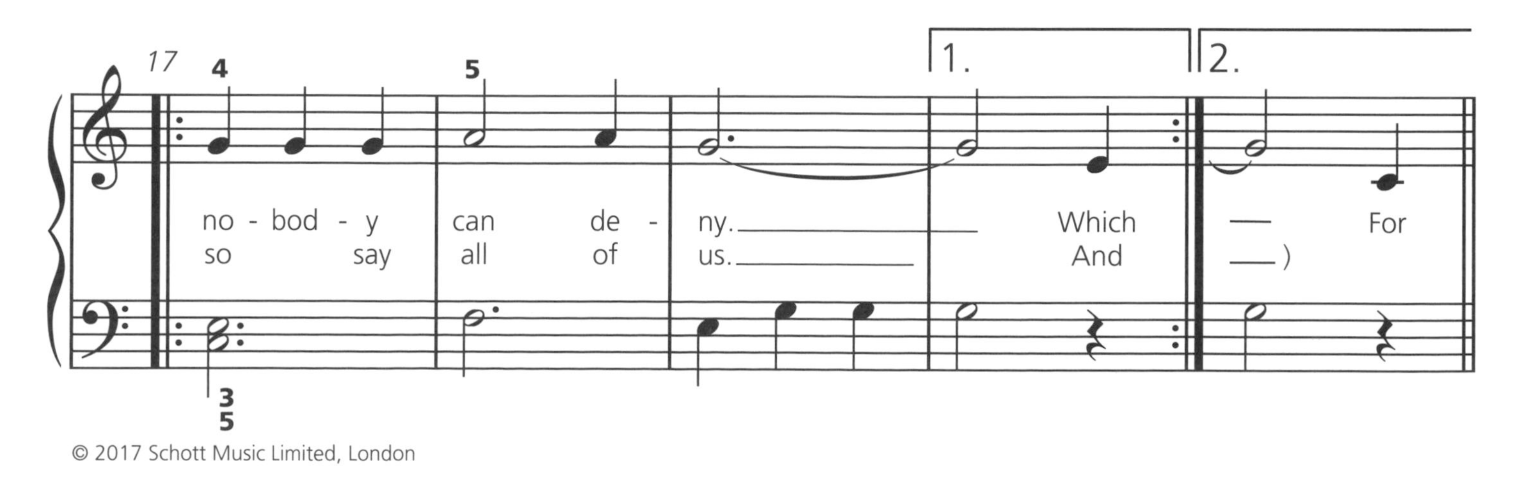

PJ

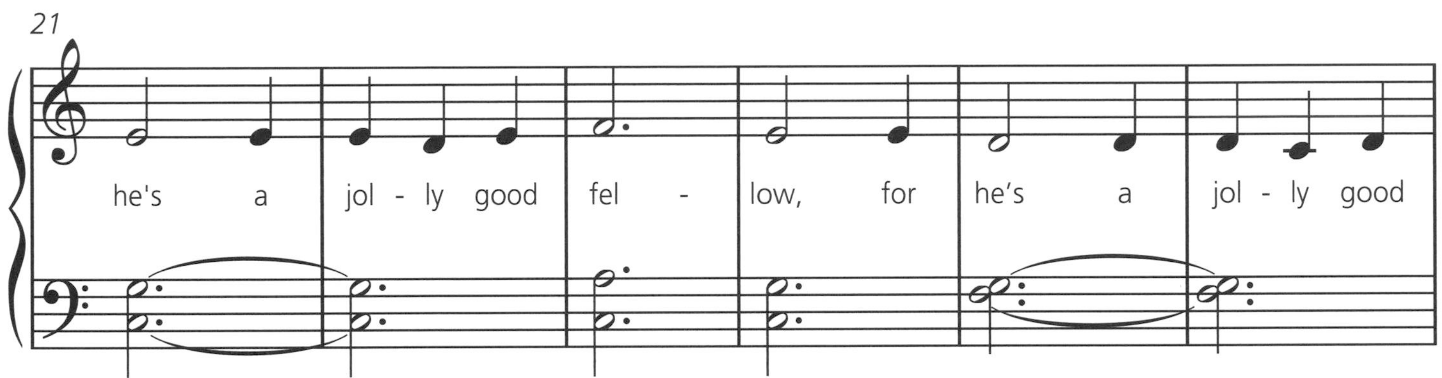
21
he's a jol - ly good fel - low, for he's a jol - ly good

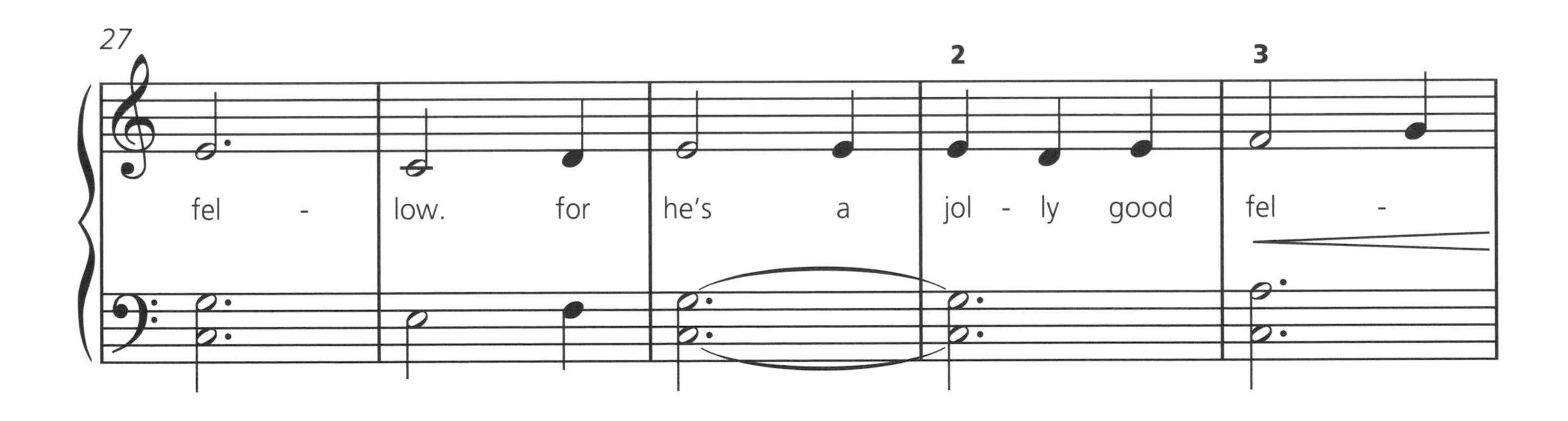
27
2
3
fel - low. for he's a jol - ly good fel -

32
4
5
- low, which no - bod - y can de - ny.
(and so say all of us.)

8. Auld Lang Syne

Scottish Folk Tune
Words by Robert Burns (1759–1796)
Arr.: HGH

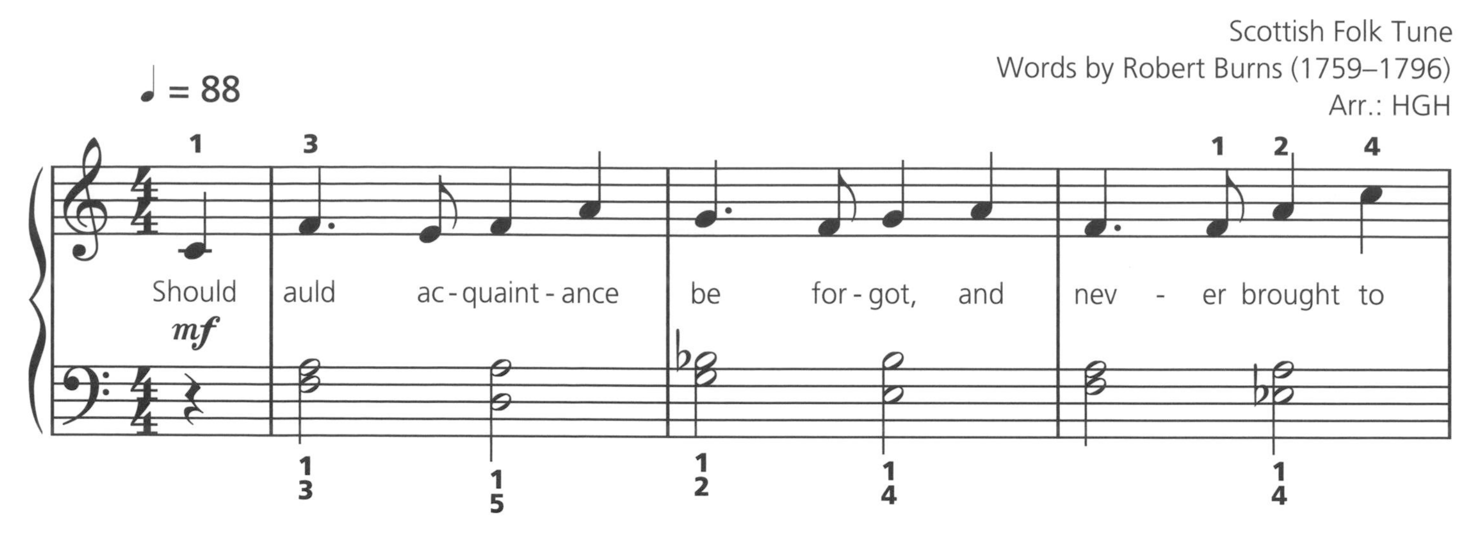

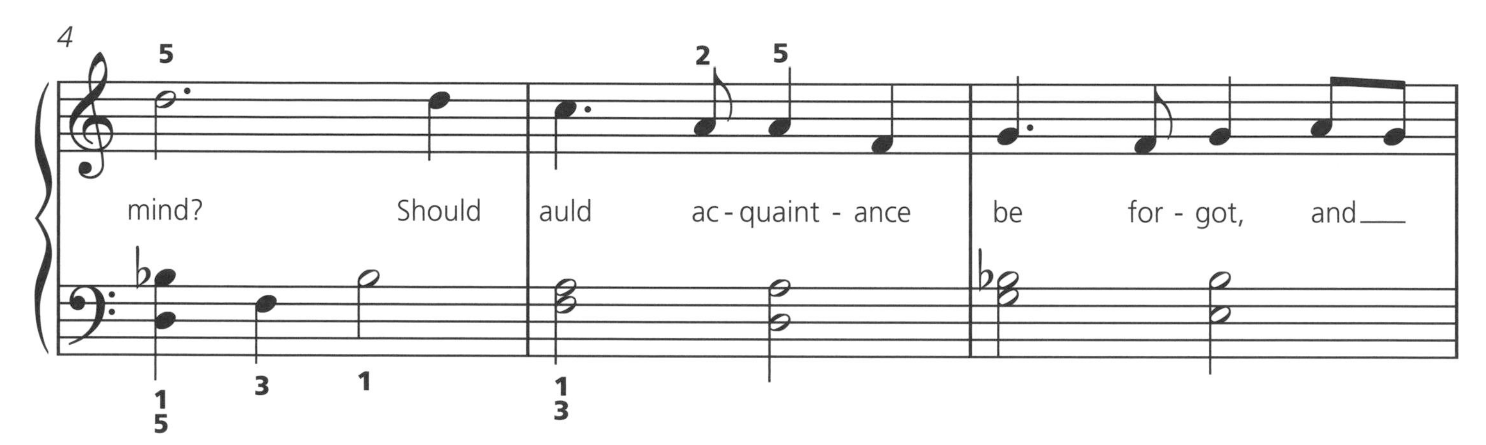

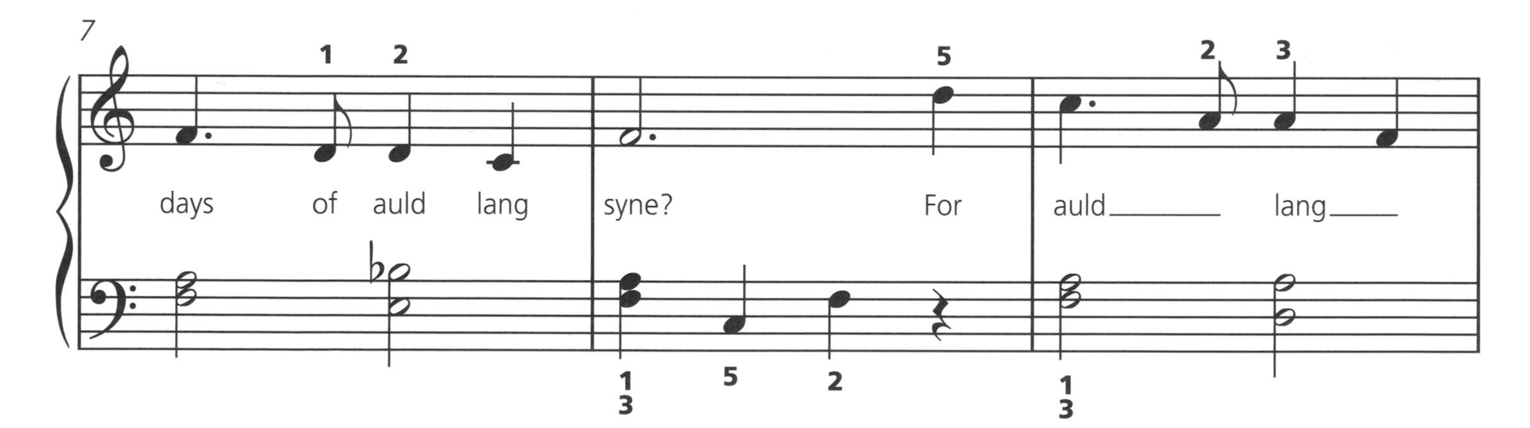

rit.
13
take a cup of kind - ness yet for auld lang syne.
p

PJ

9. Minuetto

from *24 Short and Easy Pieces*, No. 2

Alexander Reinagle was a US American pianist, piano teacher and composer of English origin.

10. Dance

♩ = 132

Johann Georg Witthauer (1750–1802)

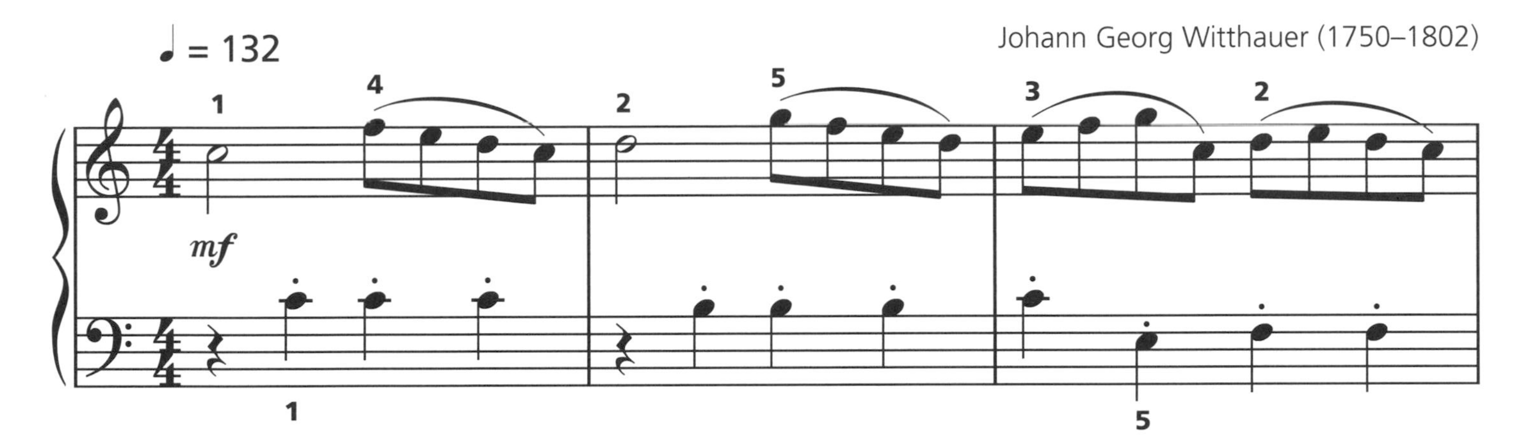

Johann Georg Witthauer was a German composer, organist and piano teacher.

11. Minuet

James Hook (1746–1827)

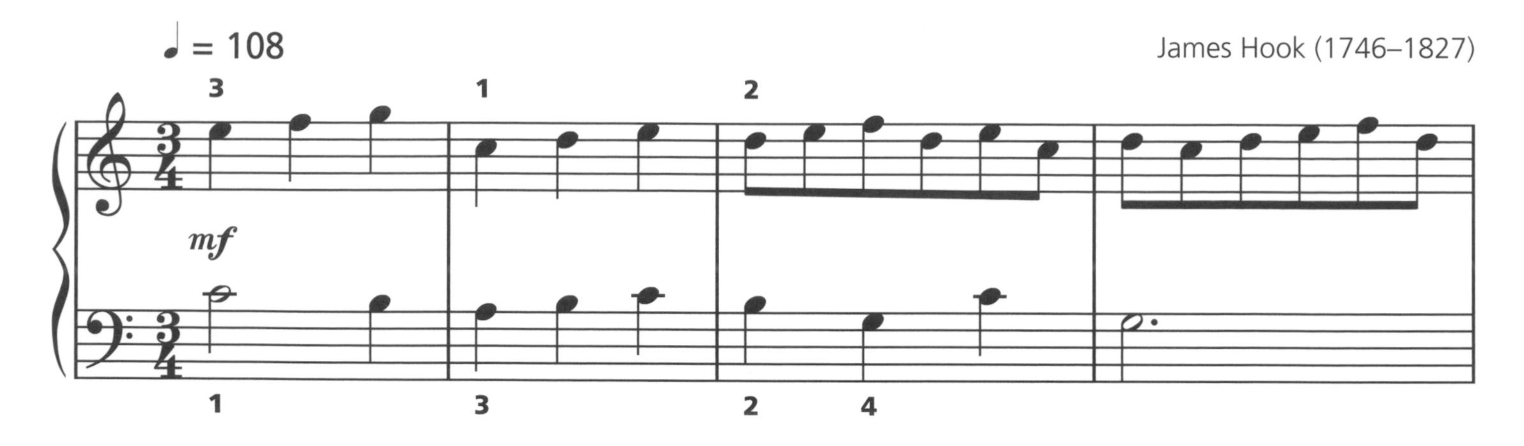

James Hook was an English composer and organist.

12. Dancing Crab

Allegretto ♩ = 126

HGH

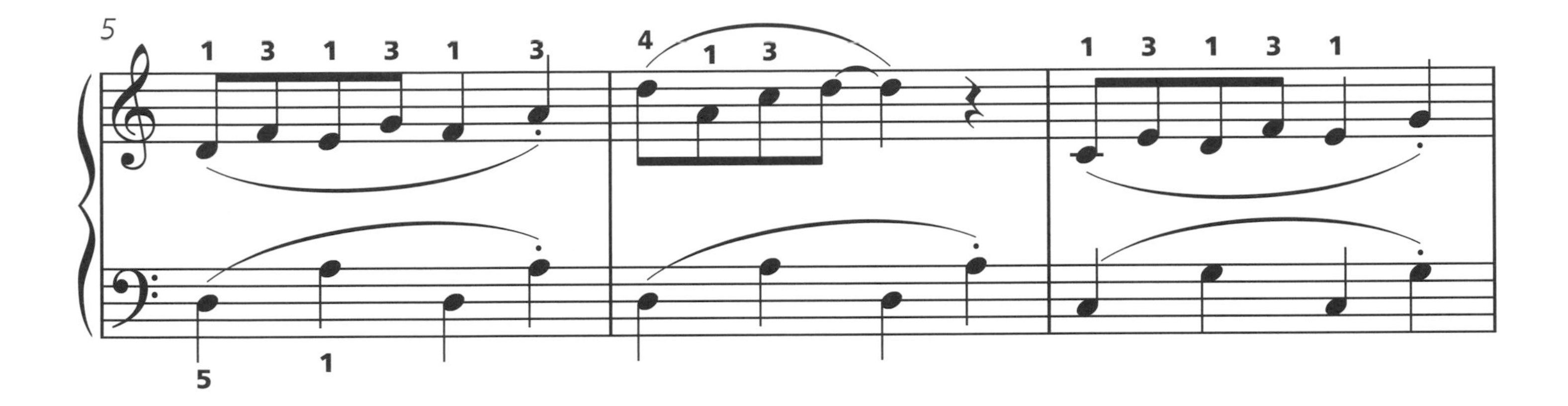

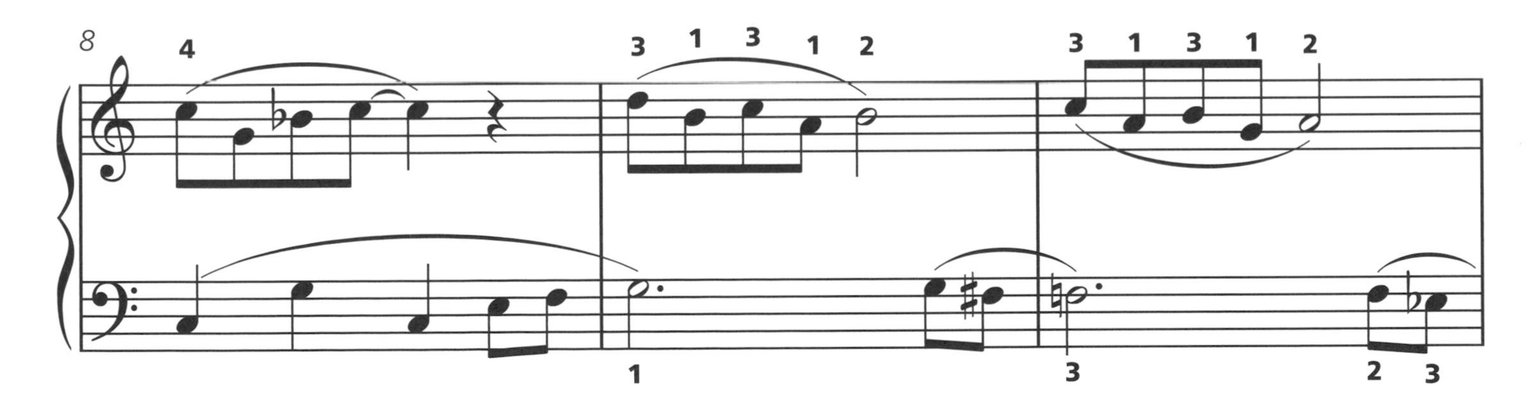

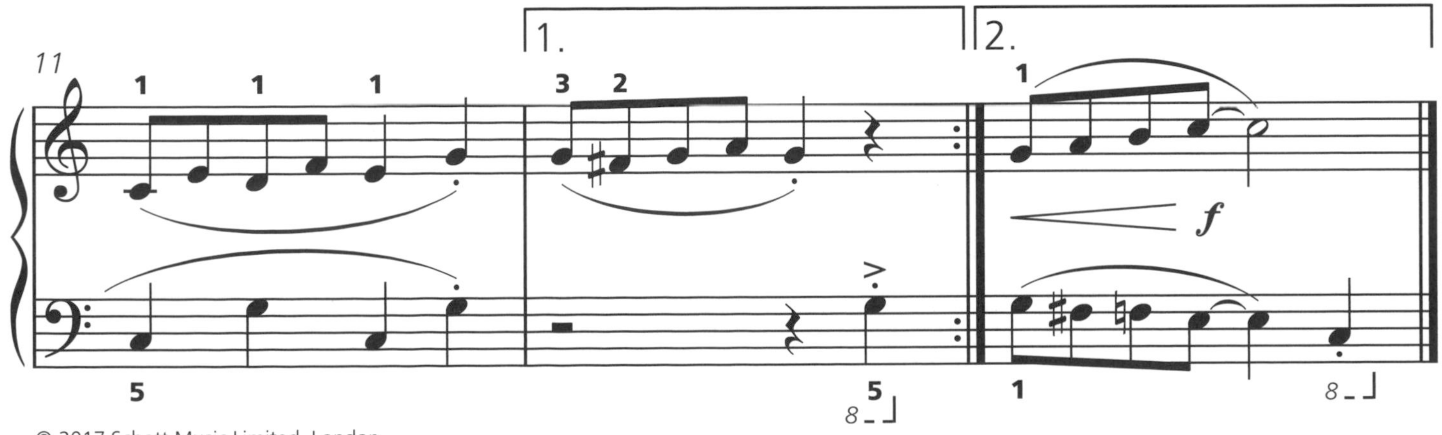

13. Flea Waltz/Chopsticks

♩ = 184

Anonymous
Arr.: HGH

14. Let's Rock

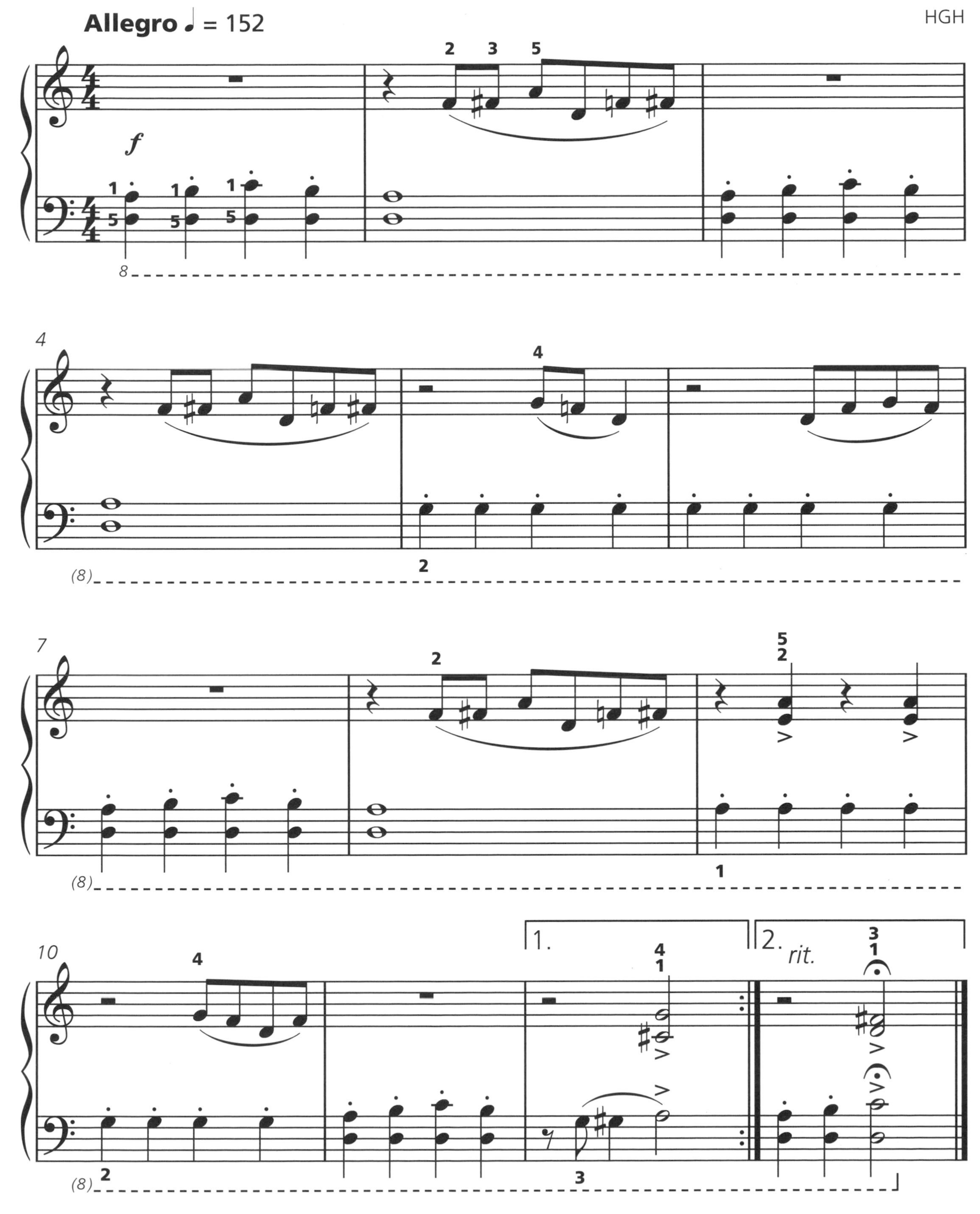

15. Dance of the Octaves

Allegro ♩ = 152

HGH

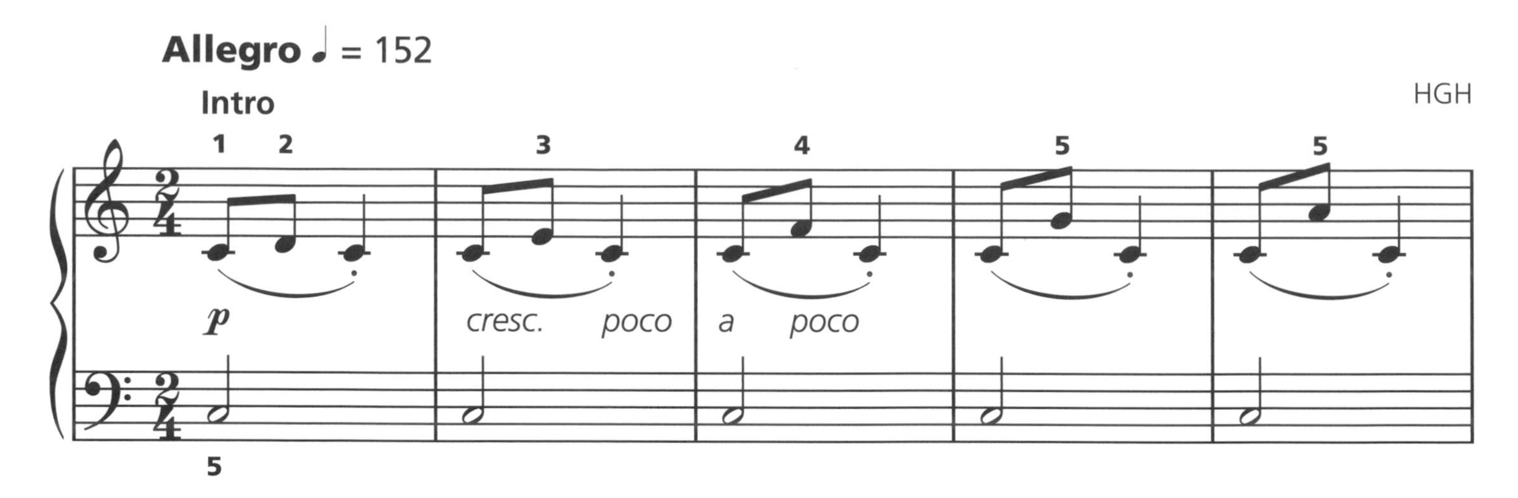

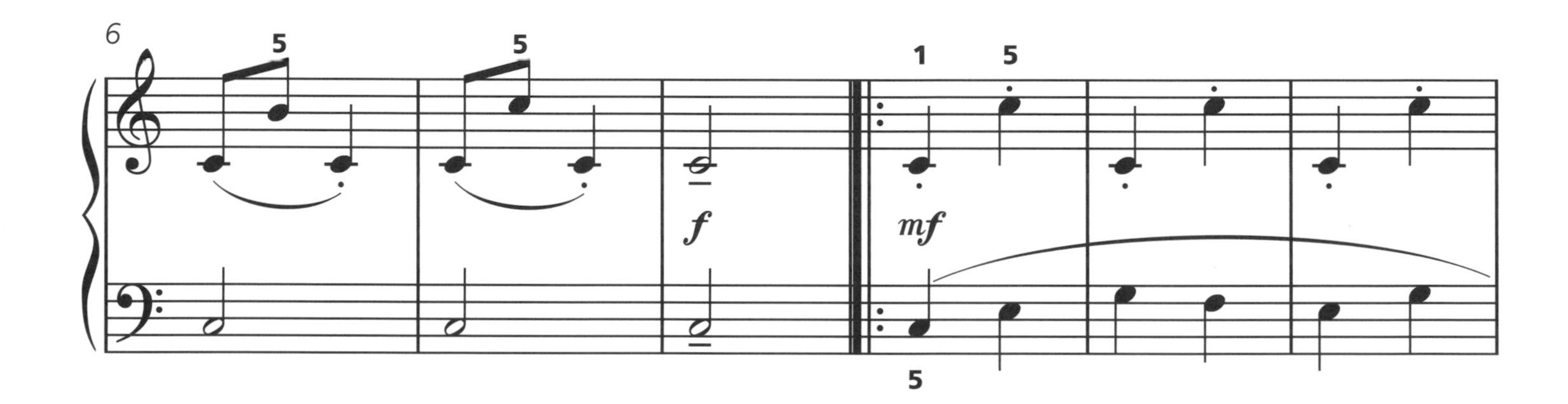

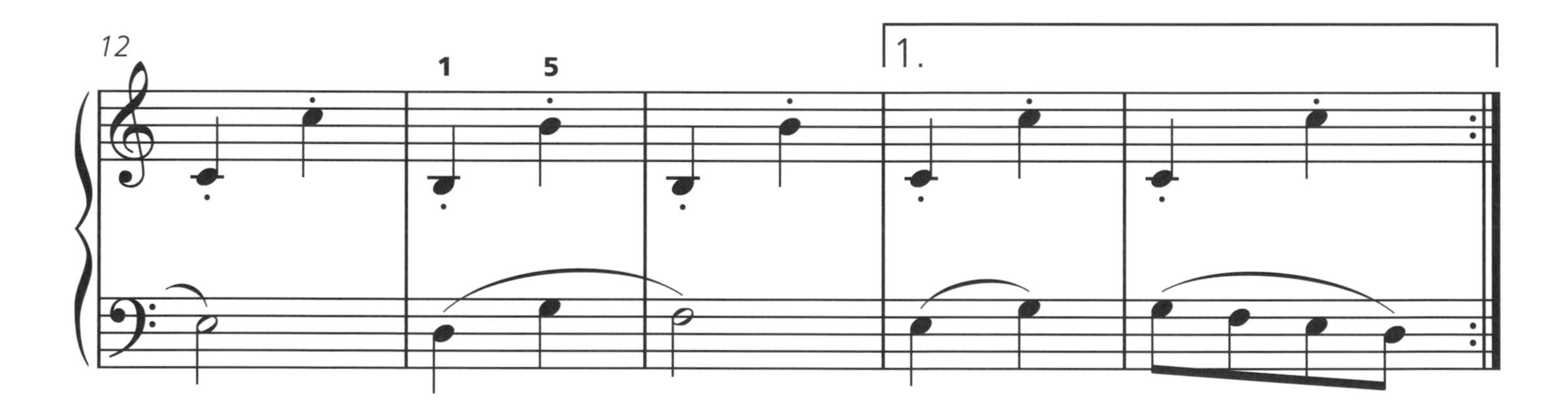

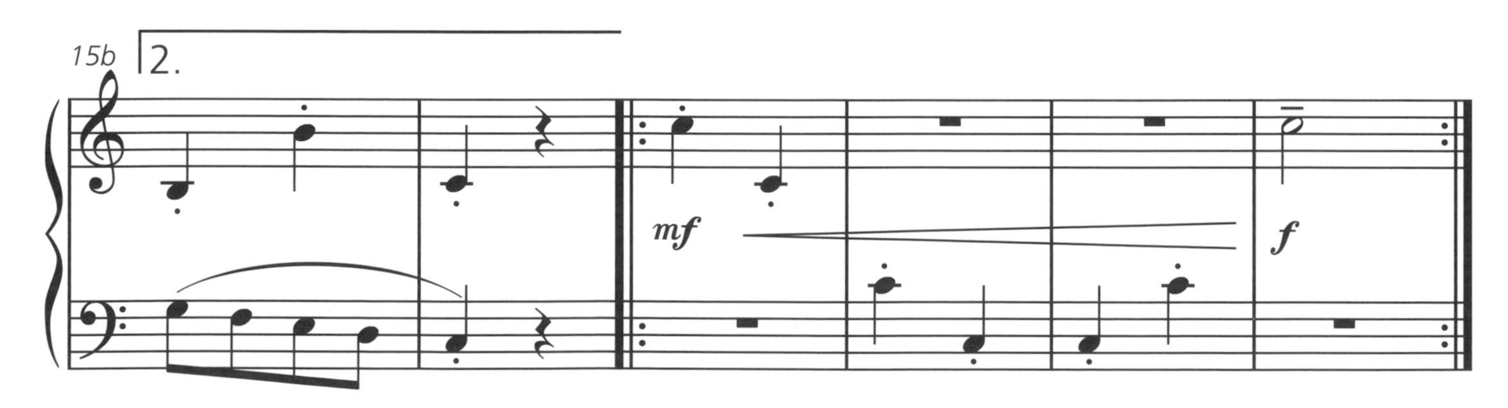

21
mf
26
1.
2.
8

16. The Birds' Wedding

German Folk Song
Arr.: HGH

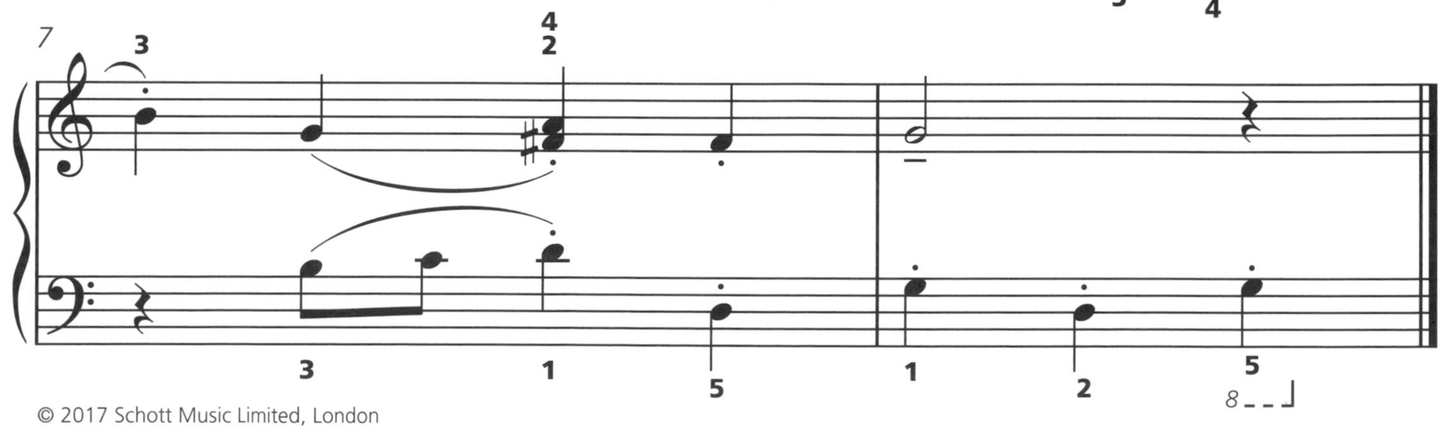

17. A Man Stands in the Forest

German Folk Song
Arr.: HGH

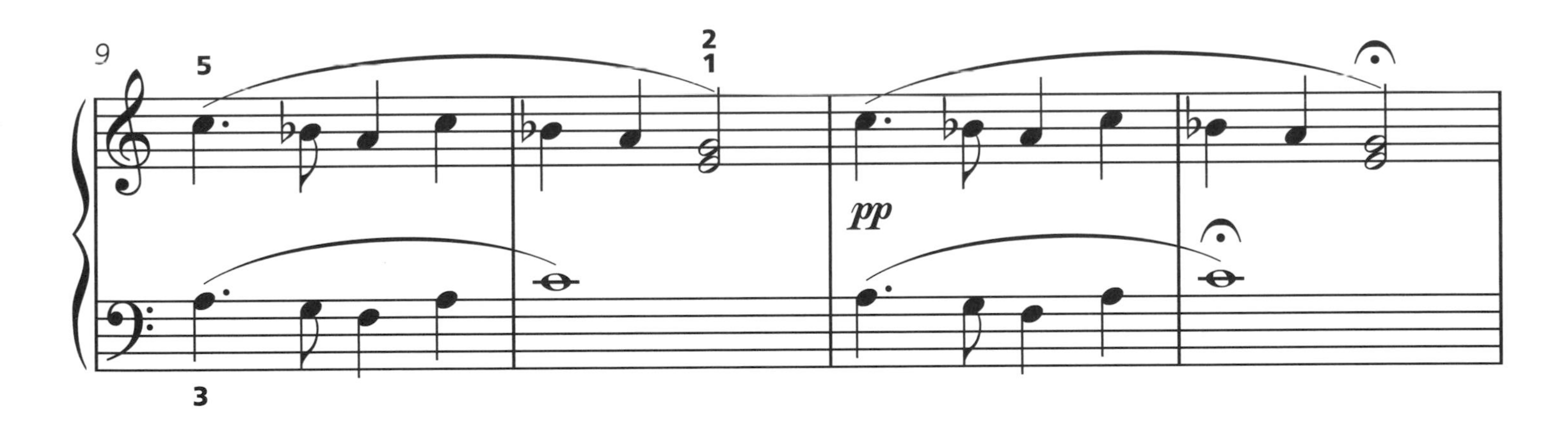

18. The Pleasure of Love

Plaisir d'amour

Words by Jean-Pierre Claris de Florian (1755–1794)
Music by Jean-Paul-Ègide Martini (1741–1816)
Arr.: HGH

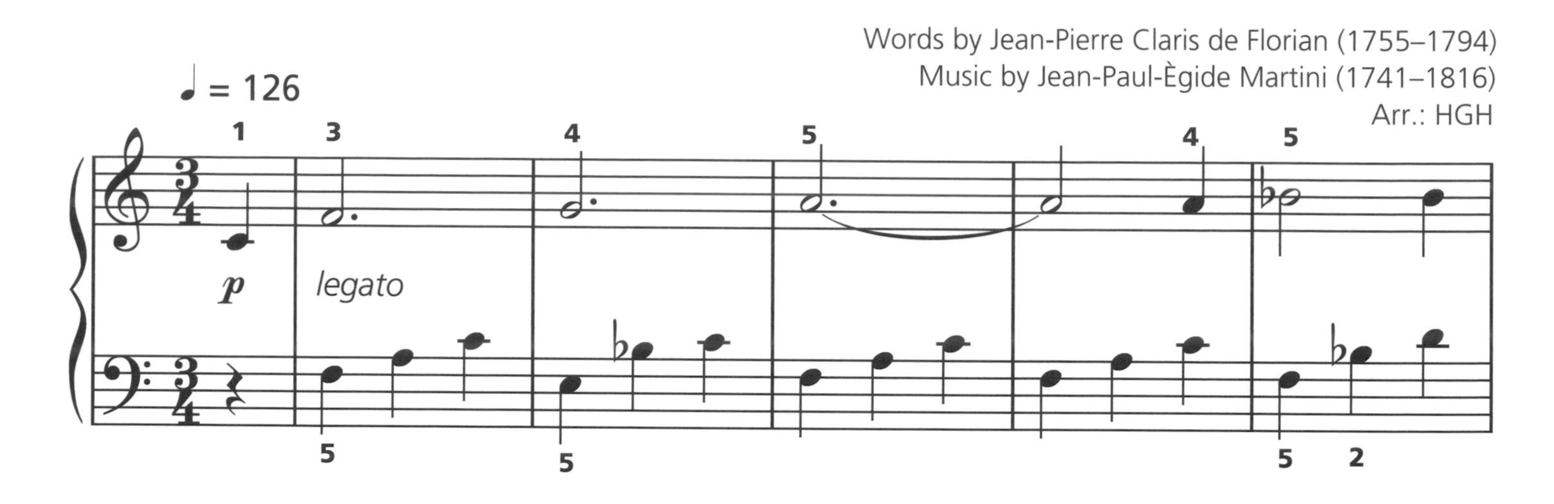

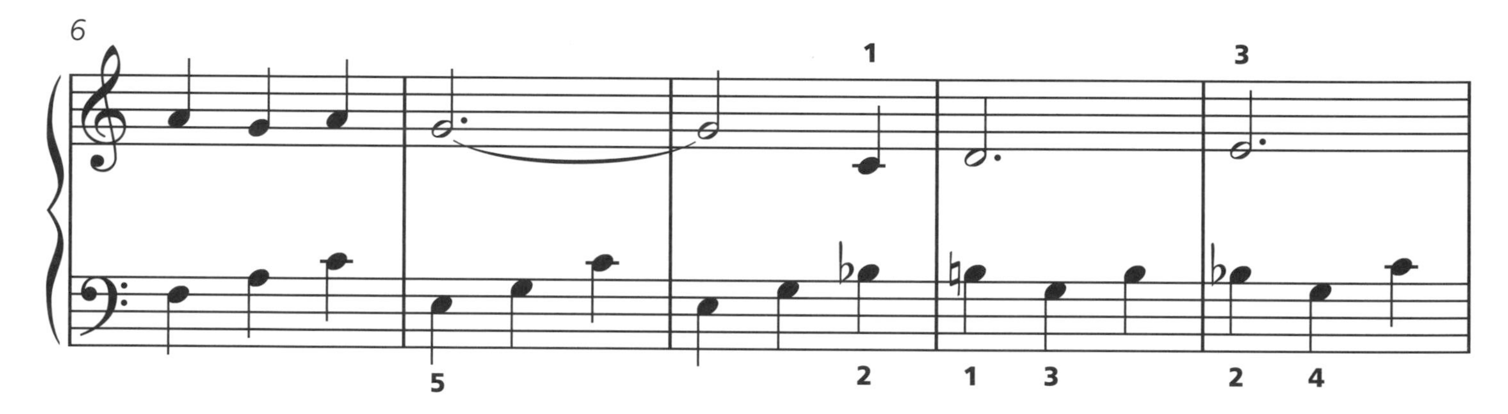

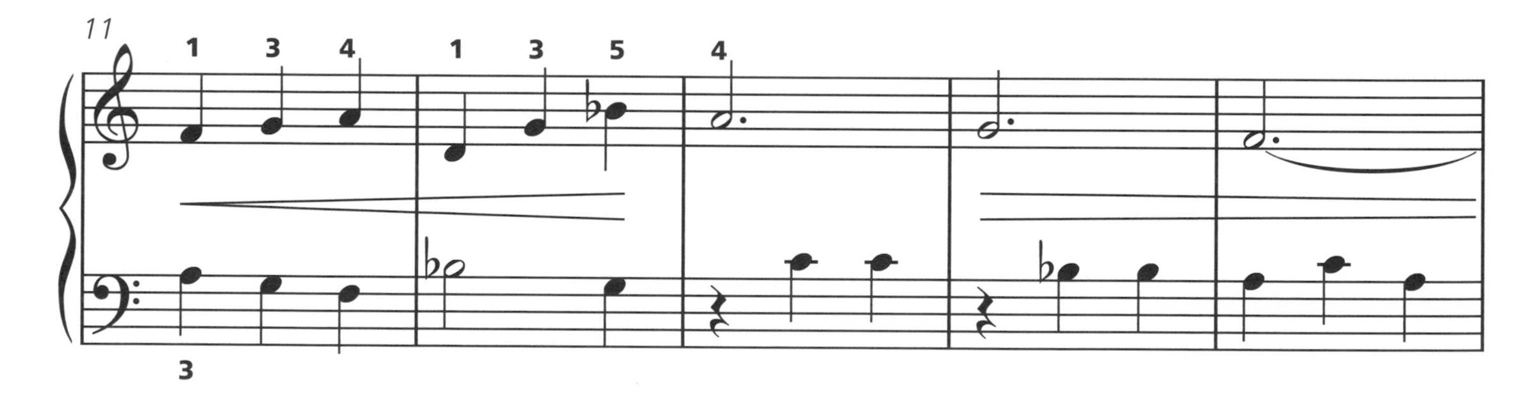

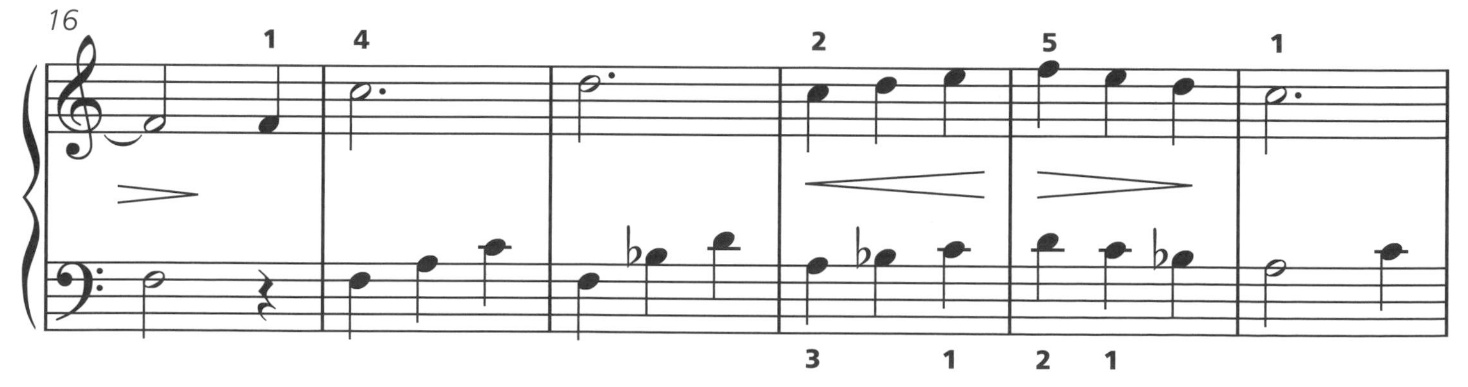

22

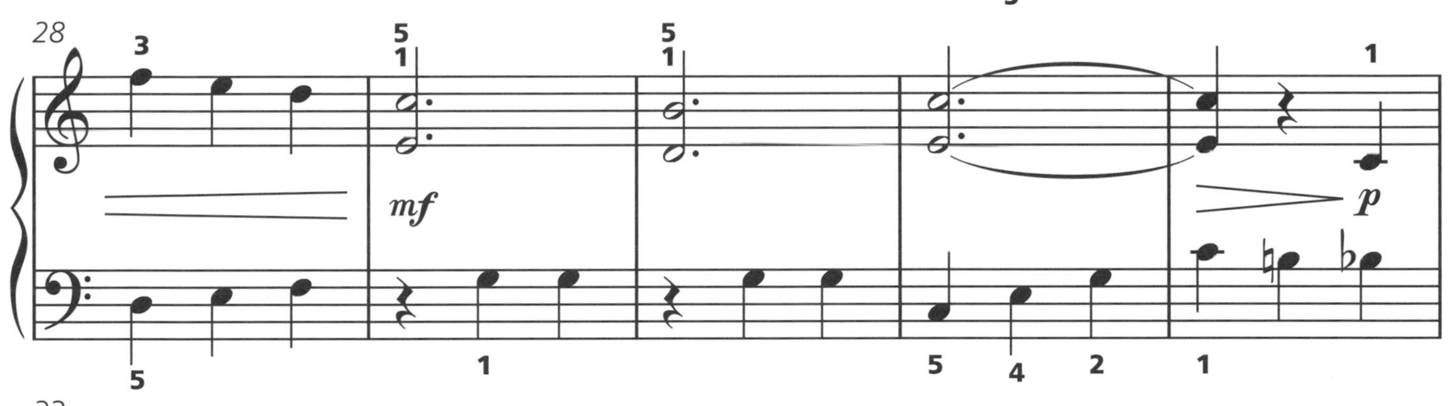
28
mf
p

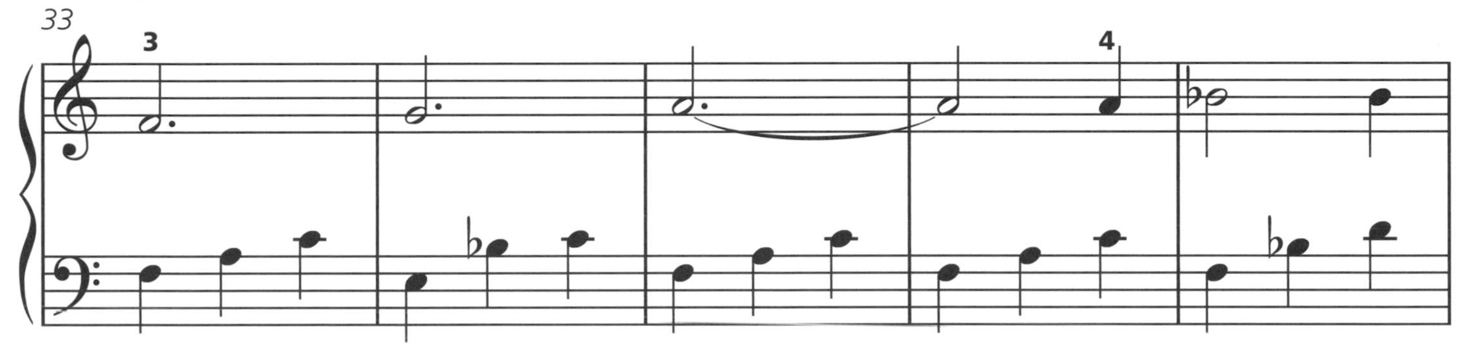
33

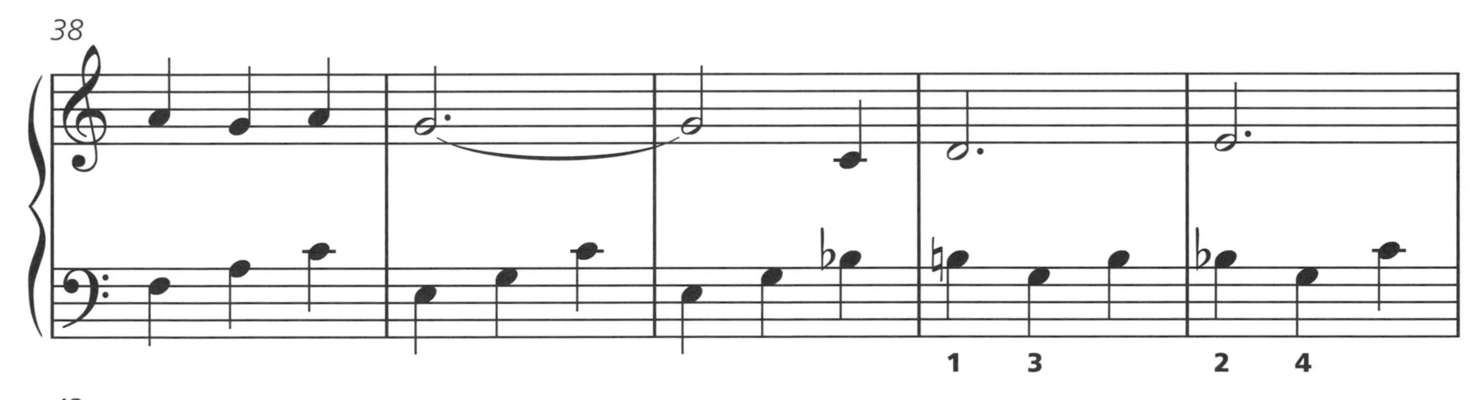
38

43
rit.

19. Scale Waltz

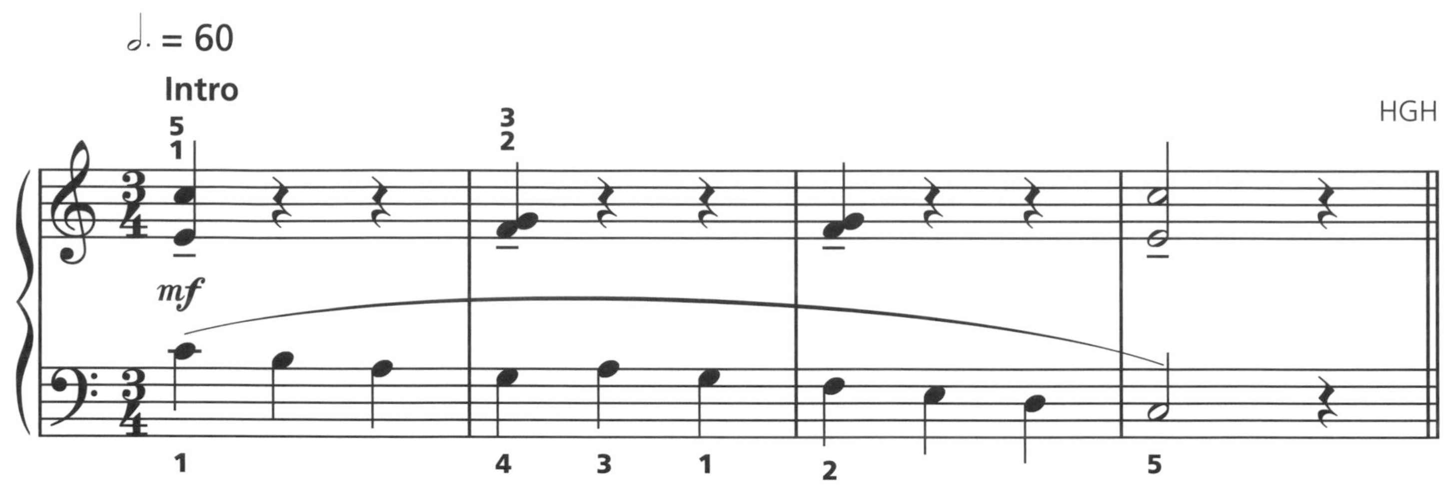

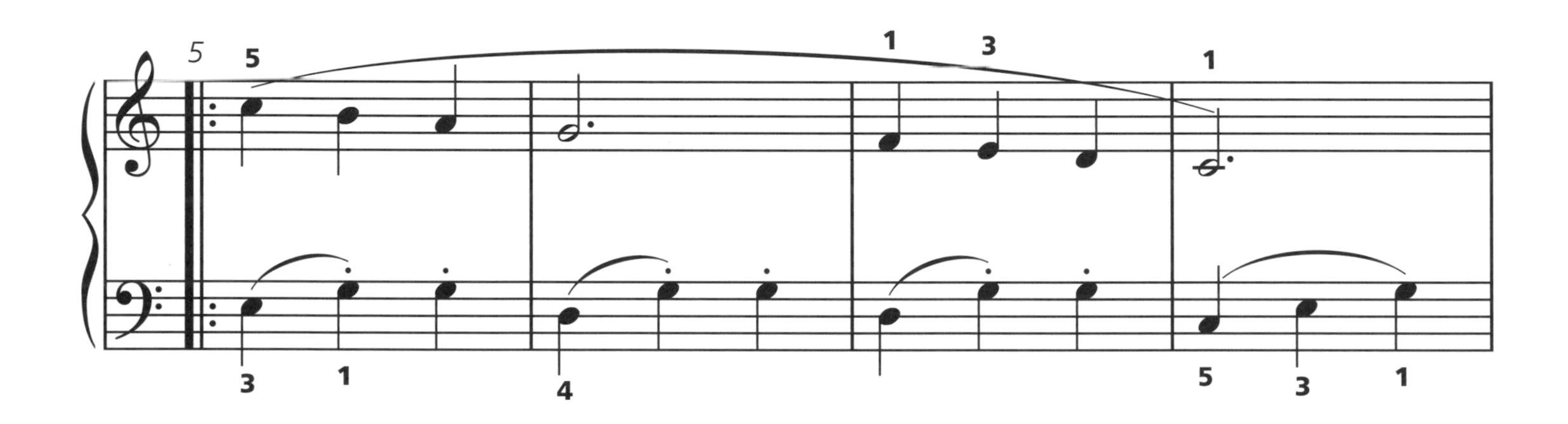

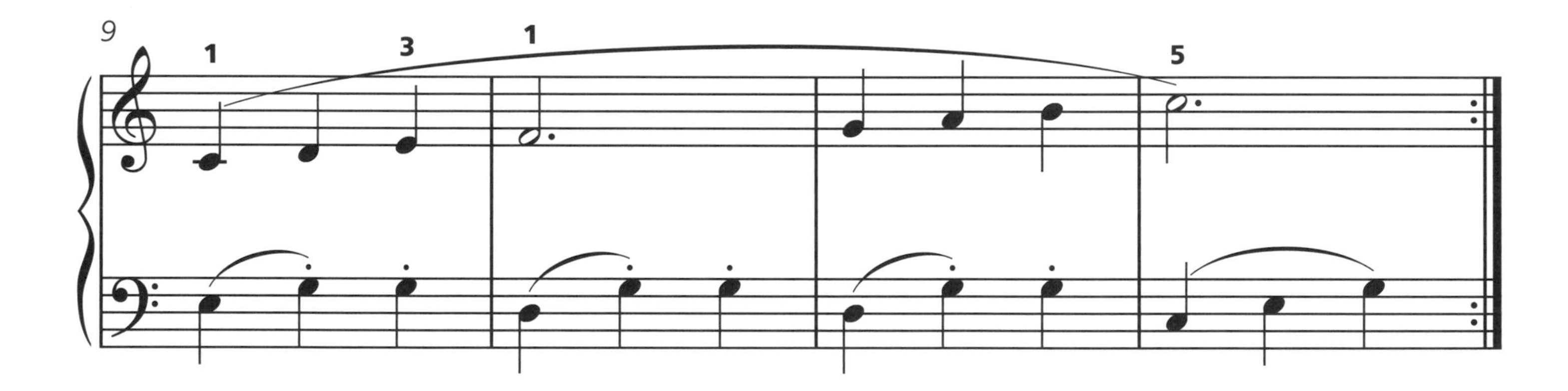

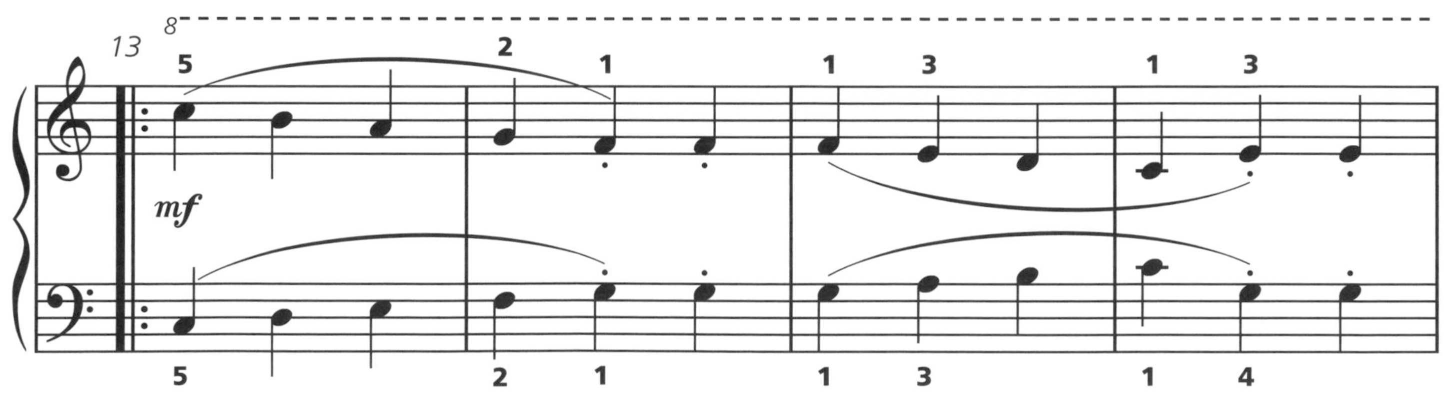

17
(8)
1.
2.
8
f
f

20. Scale Fun

Freely adapted from Op. 101, No. 65

Ferdinand Beyer (1803–1863)
Arr.: HGH

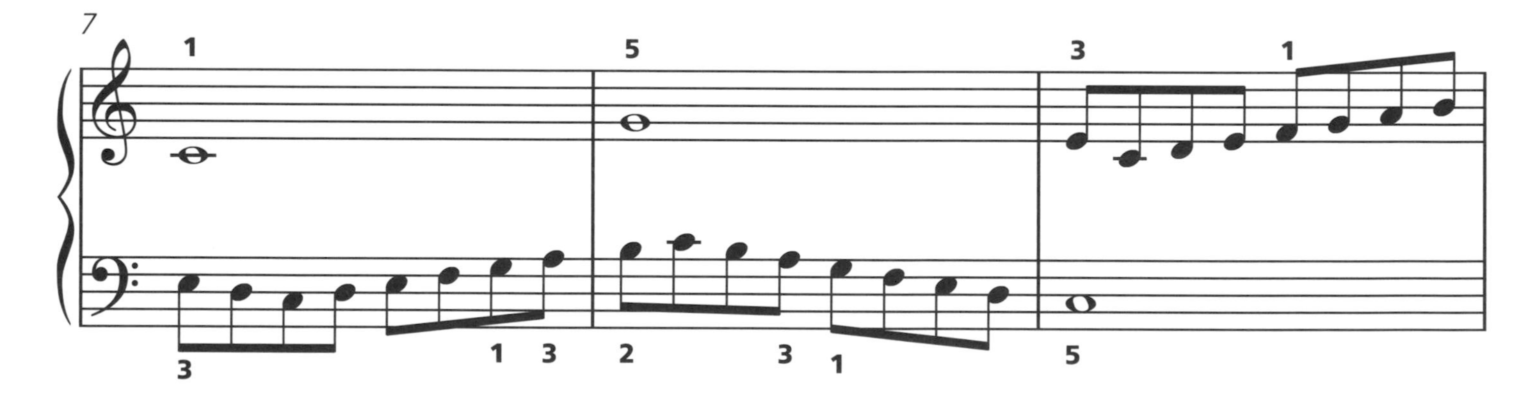

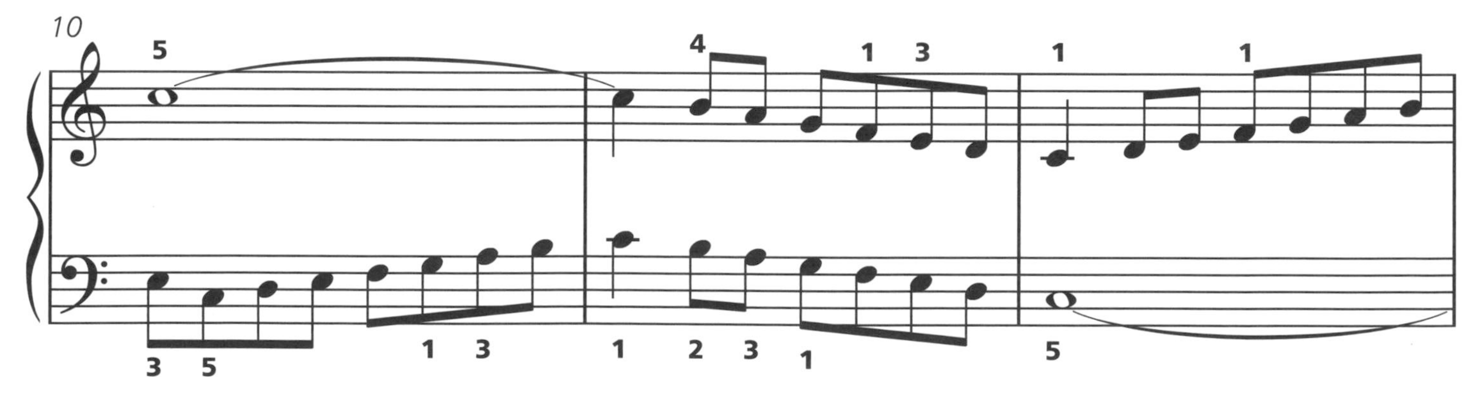

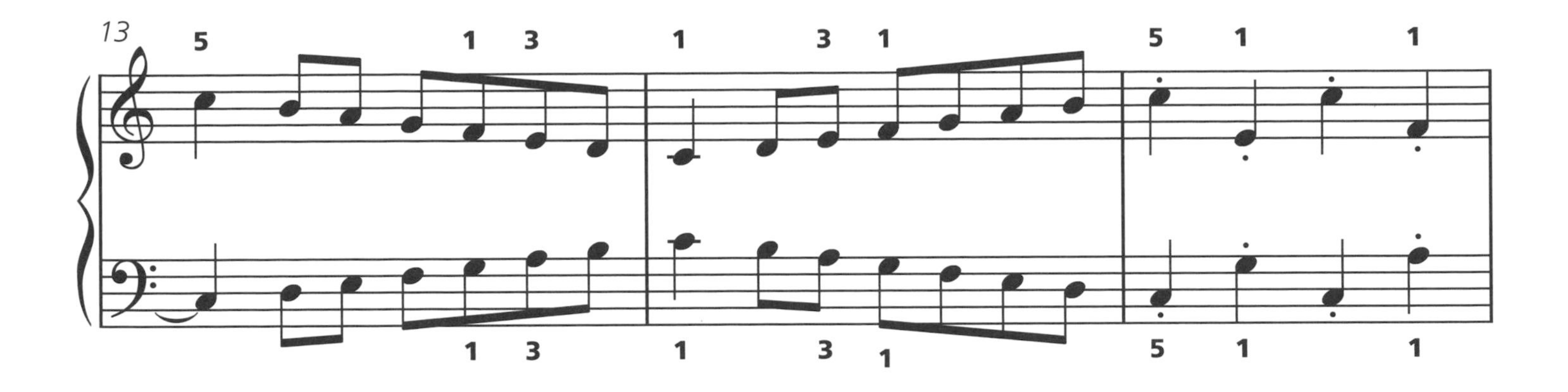

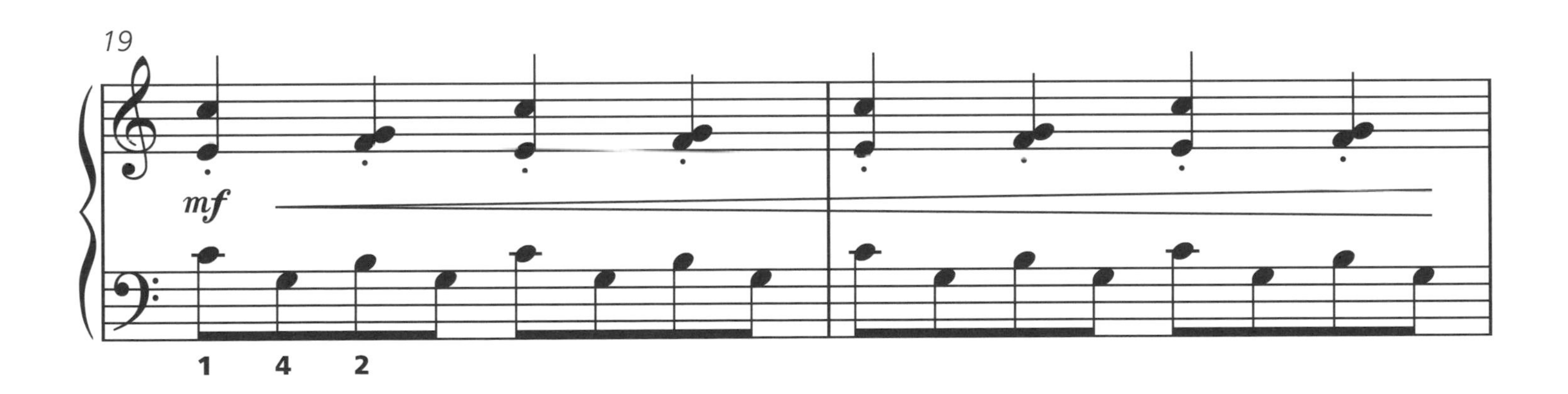

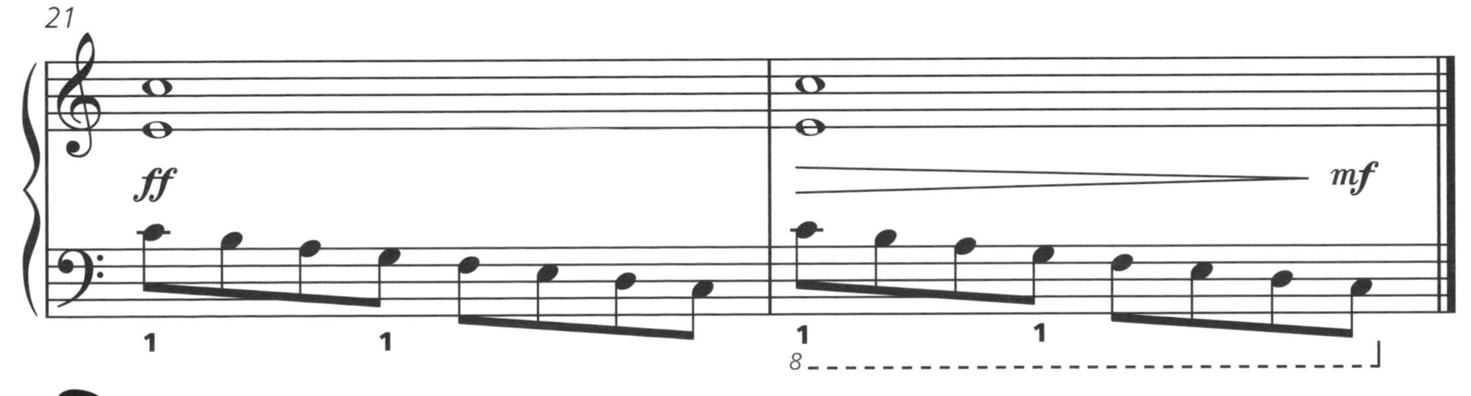

Ferdinand Beyer was a German composer, pianist and piano teacher.

21. Turkish March

from *The Ruins of Athens* Op. 113

Ludwig van Beethoven (1770–1827)
Arr.: HGH

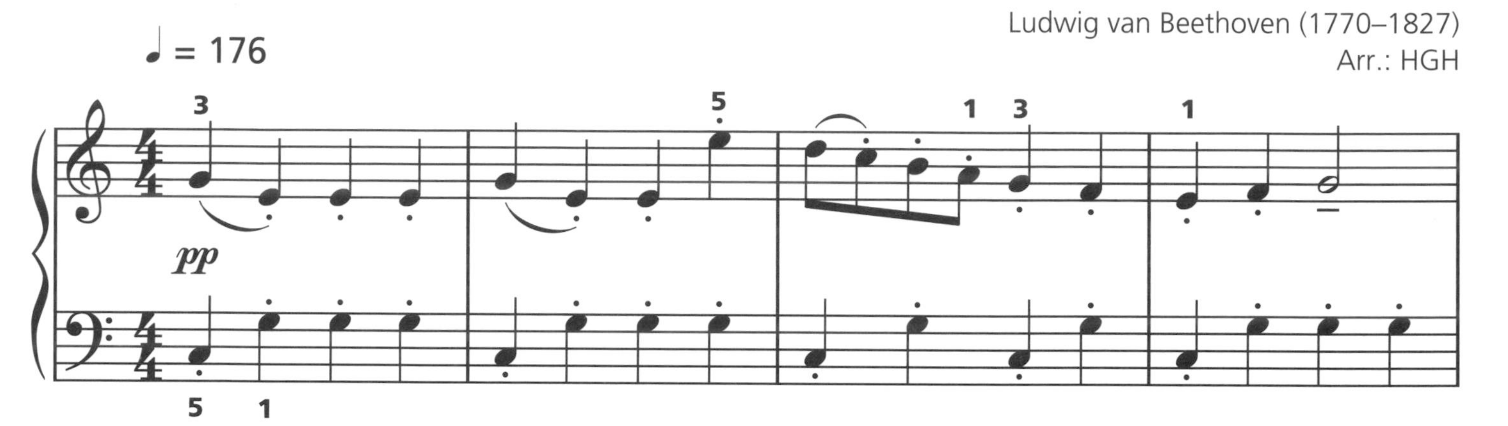

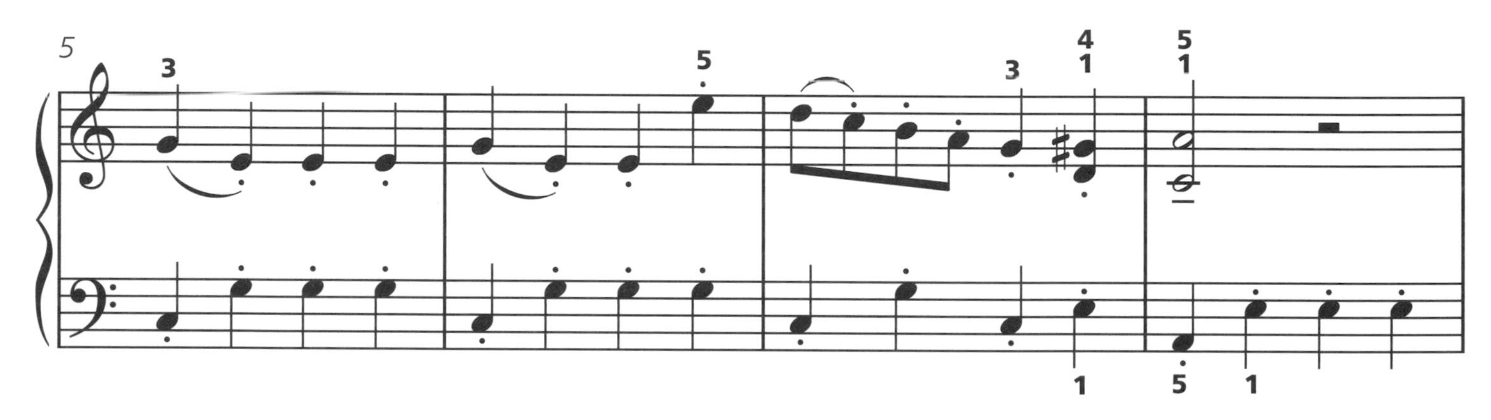

Ludwig van Beethoven was a German composer and a pupil of Joseph Haydn. His virtuoso piano playing and skill as a composer attracted numerous patrons who provided him with financial support. Despite increasing deafness, he still composed great masterpieces.

PJ

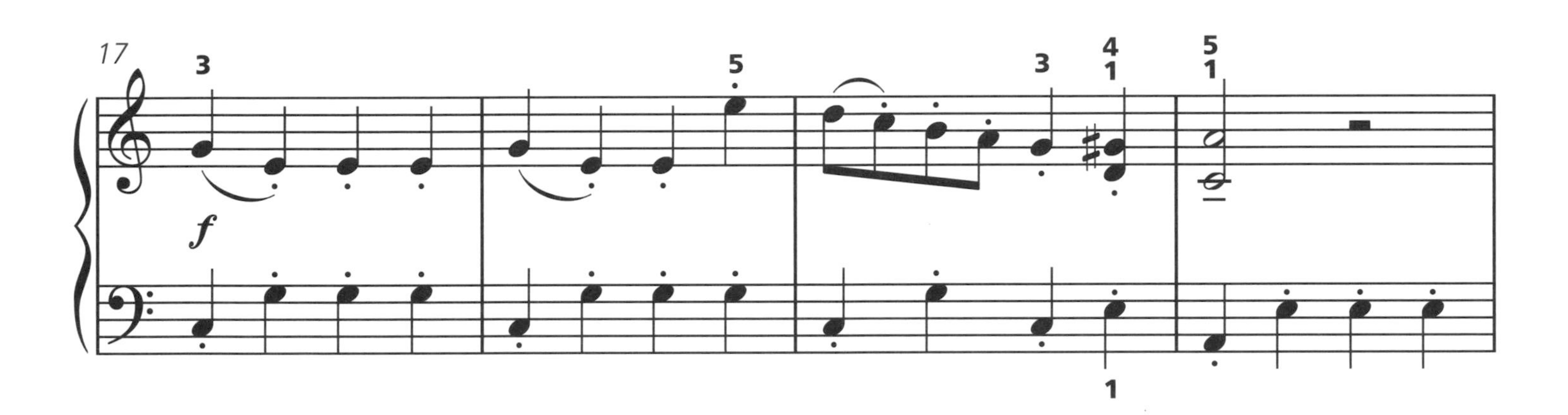
17
3
5
3
4
1
5
1
f
1

21
3
4
5

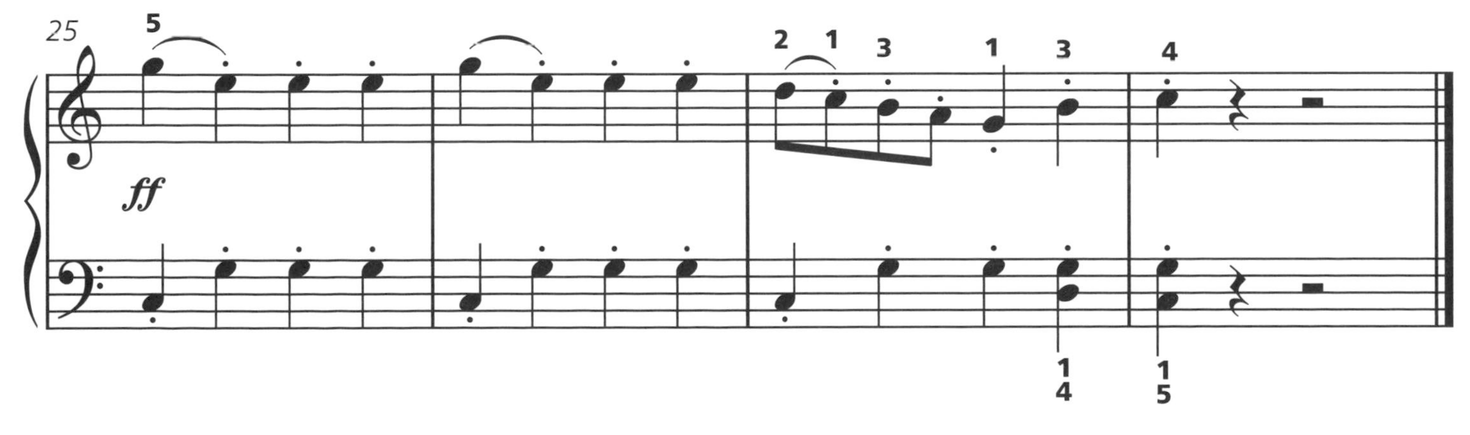
25
5
ff
2
1
3
1
3
4
1
4
1
5

22. Largo

Theme from *The New World Symphony*

*) **largo** = very slow, steady stately. A **Largo** is a piece of music with a slow, steady tempo.

Antonín Dvořák was a Czech composer. One of his best-known works is the Symphony *From the New World.*

23. Bordun Variations*

*) A **Bordun** (Fr. bourdon, Ital. bordone = low hum, humming bass) is a *drone* accompaniment using the first and fifth notes of the scale, played as the accompaniment to a melody. The bagpipes are typical drone instruments. The drone is the most simple form of polyphony.

17
1
f

21
rit.

24. Basso Ostinato*

*) **Ostinato** (Lat. ostinatus = obstinate, persistent) is a melodic or rhythmic figure, usually in the bass, which is constantly repeated; also known as *Basso Ostinato*.

25. Piano Piece

Op. 190, No. 31

Louis Köhler (1820–1886)

♩ = 144

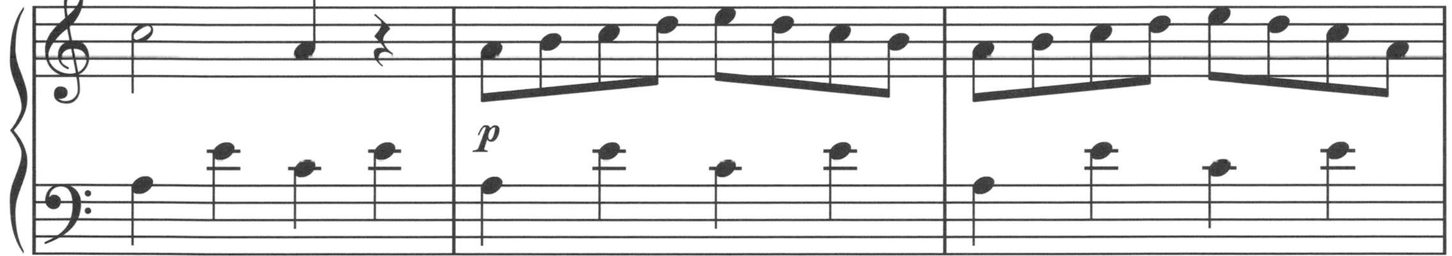

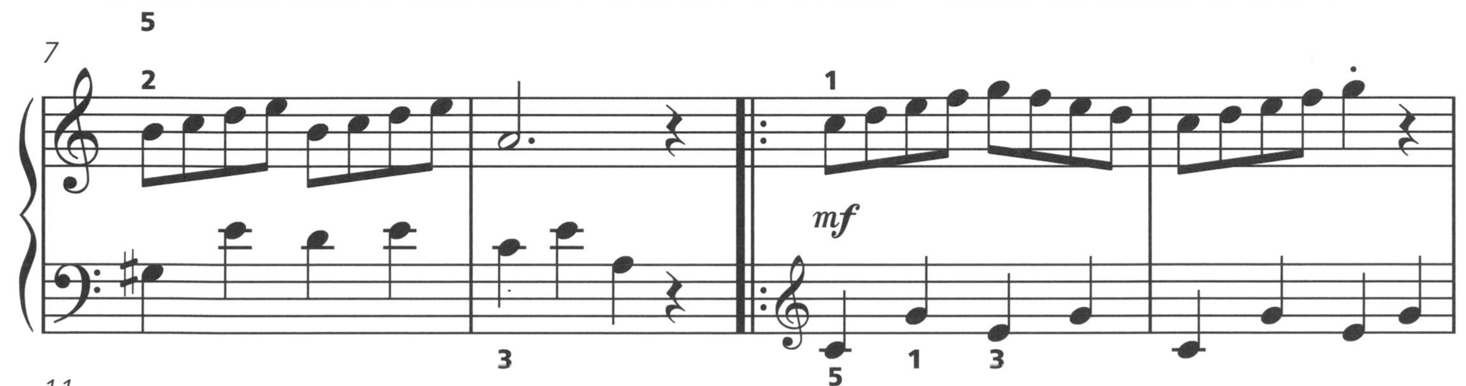

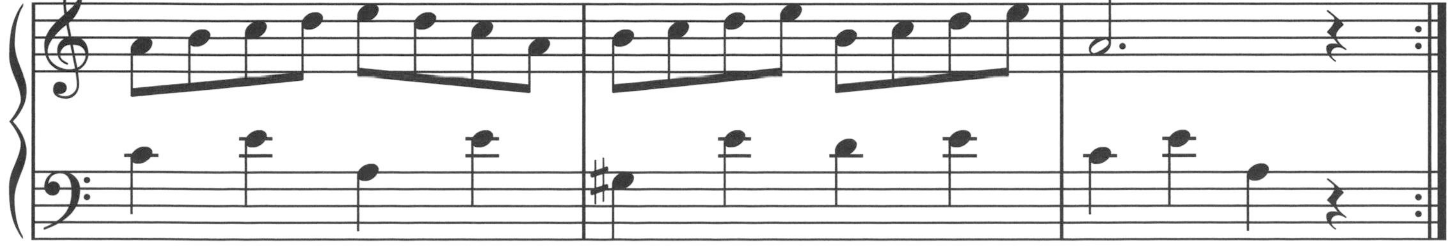

Louis Köhler was a German composer, pianist and piano teacher.